ÁLDOZATOK
ÁLDOZATOK · VICTIMS · ÁLDOZATOK
ÁLDOZATOK

Budapest, 1062
Andrássy út 60.

„The past must be acknowledged..."
(Attila József)

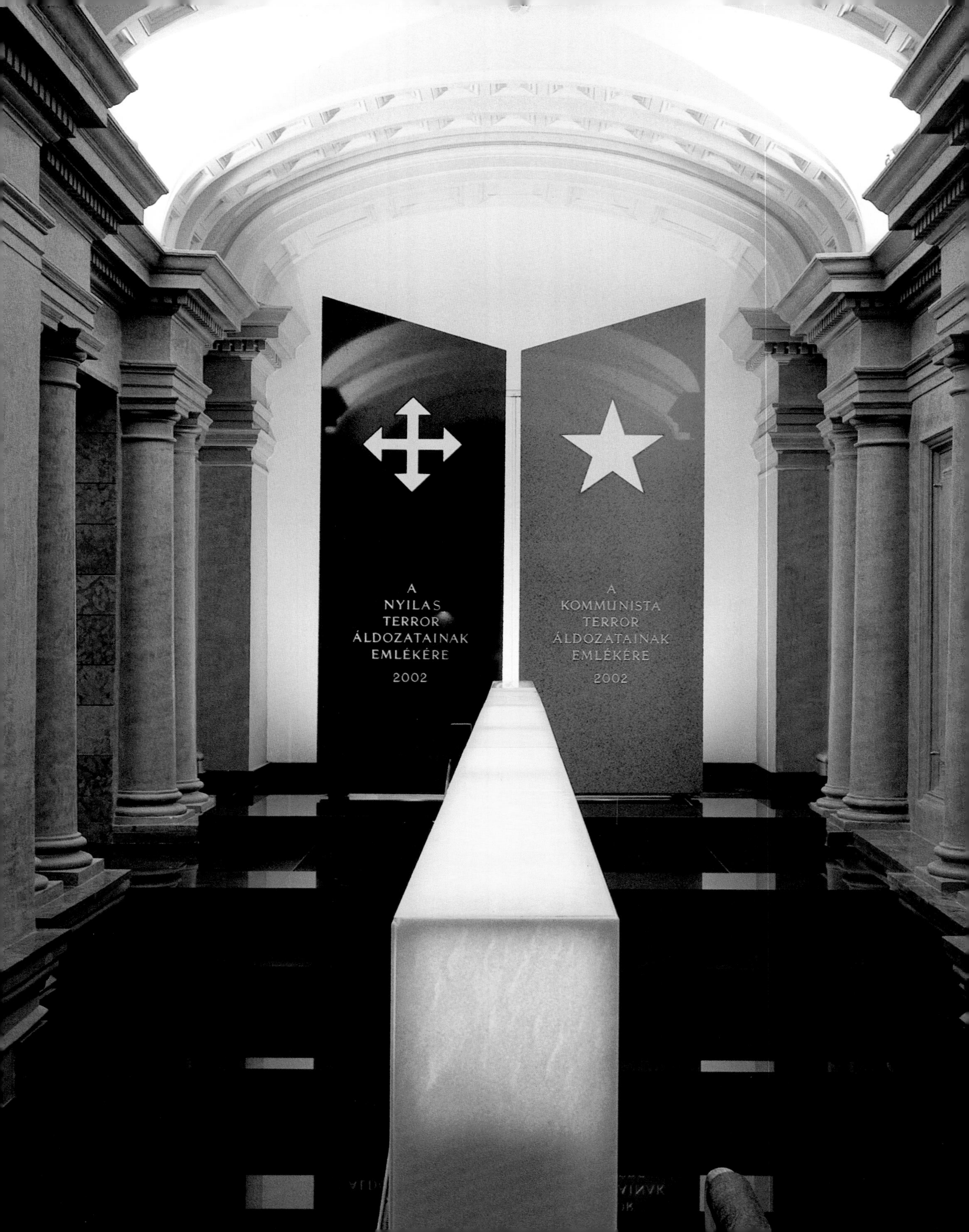
A
NYILAS
TERROR
ÁLDOZATAINAK
EMLÉKÉRE
2002
A
KOMMUNISTA
TERROR
ÁLDOZATAINAK
EMLÉKÉRE
2002

'The deeper we descend into the past, the fewer witnesses remain, oral tradition subsides into silence, memories are lost in the mists of time...'

(Solzhenitsyn)

INTRODUCTION

Andrássy Road is the capital's most beautiful thoroughfare. Straight as an arrow, flanked by marvellous mansions and dignified dwellings, this avenue connects the inner city with Heroes' Square. It was named for one of the Austro-Hungarian Monarchy's most eminent statesmen, Count Julius (Gyula) Andrássy. Oddly enough both twentieth-century terror regimes, the Arrow Cross and the communists, chose one of the buildings in this splendid avenue as the headquarters of their organs of coercion.

The neo-renaissance block which includes No. 60 Andrássy Road was built in 1880 according to the plans of the architect Adolf Feszty. In 1937, the Szálasi-wing of the Hungarian National Socialist movement began to rent more and more space in the house and the editorial office of the ultra-right newspaper "Solidarity" ("Összetartás") moved in as well.

The leader of the Arrow Cross Party, Ferenc Szálasi called the building "The House of Loyalty". In the winter of 1944, when the Hungarian Nazis came to power, hundreds of people were tortured in its basement. Expecting Hitler's wonder weapons, they sent teenage boys into senseless battles alongside the Germans, and shot innocent Jews into the half-frozen Danube. The Arrow Cross thugs' unquestioning faith in the Nazis' ultimate victory plunged the country into further destruction.

In 1945 Hungary was occupied by the Soviet Army. One of the first tasks of the Hungarian communists arriving with the Soviet tanks was to take possession of 60 Andrássy Road. The building was occupied by their secret police, the PRO (Politikai Rendészeti Osztály), which was later renamed ÁVO (Államvédelmi Osztály), subsequently ÁVH (Államvédelmi Hatóság). Gábor Péter was in charge of all of them. The entire country came to dread the former tailor and his terrorist organization. The ÁVH officers serving at 60 Andrássy Road were the masters of life and death. Detainees were horribly tortured or killed. Many of the victims died of the cruel ordeals suffered during their often week-long interrogations. Most of the prisoners, who survived the physical and psychological brutality, were eventually willing to sign any confession placed before them. As the organization outgrew the premises within a few months after moving into 60 Andrássy Road, it began to expand, and soon the whole block came under its control. The walls of the cellars beneath the buildings were broken down and the maze of cellars was transformed into a prison. No. 60 Andrássy Road remained in the ÁVH's possession until 1956.

Up to now the building blended into the row of apartment houses. By its conversion into a museum it does not merely contain an exhibition dedicated to the victims' memory; its appearance too conjures up the atmosphere of the place. For too long, for too many decades we have passed by this building with downcast eyes, with hurried steps, knowing, sensing that its walls were hiding monstrous crimes, a sea of suffering. 60 Andrássy Road has become a shrine, an homage to the victims. 60 Andrássy Road is the effigy of terror, the victims' memorial. The House of Terror Museum is proof that the sacrifice for freedom is not futile. Those who fought for freedom and independence defeated the dictatorships.

"Last night I dreamt the Germans left and no one stepped into their shoes."

(Imre Kovács)

DOUBLE OCCUPATION

The room displays the two successive foreign occupations of Hungary. One part of the monitor-wall depicts the genocidal Nazi régime: Hitler and the jubilant crowds, as well as the horrifying photographs of Bergen-Belsen, while on the other side we can see the Red Army, the signing of the Molotov-Ribbentrop Pact and military parades along Red Square. There are some shots of the Hungarian Army's participation in the war against the Soviet Union, as well as of the siege of Budapest. The pictures on the walls of the hall portray the devastation caused by the war in Hungary. The four interconnected plasma monitors let us follow the transformation of Central Europe from the First World War to the end of World War II.

Hungary was defeated in the First World War. The peace dictated by the victorious powers in the Trianon Palace at Versailles deprived the country - whose area had once been larger than that of Italy and England – of two-thirds of its territory. The provisions of the treaty resulted in more than three million Hungarians being placed under the jurisdiction of neighbouring countries. As a consequence of the World War and the subsequent revolution, followed by the Bolshevik putsch, Hungary was plunged into a hopeless economic situation. Isolated politically, disarmed, encircled by hostile countries, she became one of Central Europe's weakest, most vulnerable states. Territorial revision by peaceful means and the reinstatement of the historical Hungary became the focus of her policy. As the neighbouring successor states regarded Hungarians as their principal external and internal enemies, the millions of Hungarians forced into minority status were subjected to hitherto unsurpassed oppression.

From the mid-thirties onward, Hungary found herself in the buffer zone between the increasingly more aggressive Nazi Germany and the Soviet Union, which by the end of the decade once again became a power to reckon with. Allied with one another, and subsequently locked in a life-and-death battle, the two totalitarian dictatorships strove for a new order that had no place for an independent Hungary. After the outbreak of World War II, Hungary made desperate attempts in order to maintain her – albeit limited – elbow-room and to avert the worst scenario: German occupation. It was a great achievement that this eventuated only in the fifth year of the war, on March 19, 1944.

On June 26, 1941 Kassa, Munkács and Rahó suffered bomb attacks. According to contemporary reports the bombardment was the work of the Soviet air force (although this question has not been satisfactorily clarified to this very day). Regent Horthy declared a state of war between Hungary and the Soviet Union. During 1941 and 1942 some two hundred and fifty thousand Hungarian soldiers fought on the Eastern Front. In 1943 Hungarian troops suffered heavy losses inflicted by the Red Army.

Up to the time of the Nazi occupation of 1944, Hungary's affairs were conducted by an elected, legitimate parliament and government, with representatives of active opposition parties sitting in the chambers. Despite wartime restrictions, freedom of the press was upheld. Hungarian citizens lived a better and freer life than their neighbours. After March 19, however, the country received a foretaste of what would have been its lot had the Nazis won the war. Hitler's Germany occupied Hungary in order to secure absolute control over the country's material and human resources in the interests of "final victory". Real power rested in the hands of Edmund Veesenmayer, the German plenipotentiary. The Nazis installed a puppet-government and embarked on crushing the spirit of the Hungarian people.

After the Germans occupied Hungary, the National Socialist "regulation of the Jewish question", the "final solution" took its course with the active co-operation of the Hungarian authorities. The Jews, who had already suffered from the restrictions of the Jewish Laws enacted in 1938, 1939 and 1941, were now in direct peril of their lives. Measure after measure – time-tested all over Europe by "experts", members of the infamous Judenkommando – succeeded each other with lightning speed. The decree ordering Jews to wear the yellow star was followed by the worst possible scenario: on May 15, 1944 the dreaded deportation trains began to roll. Within two months 437,402 Jews from country regions were transported to labour- i.e. death-camps under the jurisdiction of the Third Reich.

On August 27, 1944 Soviet troops crossed the Hungarian border. The country became the theatre of war in the clash between the two Super Powers. The short, but disastrous Nazi occupation was followed by Soviet rule, which established itself for a long duration. Hungary's sovereignty was lost on March 19, 1944. Occupying forces were stationed on its soil for over four decades. The last Soviet soldier, Viktor Silov, left our country on June 19, 1991.

KITARTÁS
JÖVÜNK

"I assumed power on October 16 fully and definitely convinced of victory."

(Ferenc Szálasi, 1946)

THE ARROW CROSS CORRIDOR

On the wall we can see Ferenc Szálasi's "Report to the Nation", which he published after the putsch of October 1944. Opposite is an Arrow Cross poster, and next to it a photo showing the exhumation of the victims of the Maros Street mass murder. (Armed units of the 12th district Arrow Cross organization massacred Jewish patients and staff of the Maros-street hospital.) A frieze of Arrow Cross insignia frames the walls of the corridor, similarly to the way they were used as decorations in the "House of Loyalty".

On March 18, 1944, Hitler invited Hungary's Regent, Miklós Horthy and, exploiting his absence, ordered the country's occupation, a move he had already decided on earlier. Our fatherland now faced a tragic situation. The new government handed over the countryside's Jewish population to the Nazi's murderous racial hatred. The majority was deported to Auschwitz. Almost all of them perished.

By the end of summer it became evident that Germany had lost the war. The Allies were pushing forward relentlessly in the West as well as the East. On August 29, Horthy dismissed the government led by Döme Sztójay, replacing him by his faithful confidant, Géza Lakatos, whom he entrusted with the task of preparing to extricate Hungary from the war. A secret armistice delegation travelled to Moscow, to arrange the terms of Hungary's capitulation. In a proclamation read over the radio on October 15, Horthy acquainted the nation with the fact that Hungary had asked for a ceasefire. The Nazis, however, thwarted the mismanaged attempt at defection, placed Horthy in "protective custody" and put in power an Arrow Cross government under Ferenc Szálasi.

Ferenc Szálasi: "Report to the Nation" (selection from his proclamation)

"The perilous condition of our Hungarian fatherland, the wretched hardship of the working people, unresolved welfare issues, as well as the circumstance that our nation had of late been bogged down in the utter lack of leadership and that the men in control of the state neither could, nor wanted to secure victory, has rendered it imperative that profound and decisive changes should take place. In order to defend the country and its people, to create prosperity and security, to gain victory, to attain our fitting place in a nationalist and socialist Europe, the country has decided on the total mobilization of its resources, the radical liquidation of the old regime and the establishment of the Hungarian national socialist political and social order. (...) The nation, with its new leadership in the vanguard will fight valiantly to secure the defence and safety of the country and its people, standing loyally on the side of its allies, in the same spirit with which Germany, the fighting Italy and Japan is striving to create a new world. (...) We consider all sacrifice made for the sake of victory as insufficient, we shall willingly shoulder even the most bloody and grave sacrifices in the service of our country. Anyone who sabotages the population's endeavours in any shape or form, anyone who undermines stability, leaves his workplace, does not perform his job with the utmost responsibility thereby impeding the attainment of our goals, shall forfeit his life."

"I have called down fire and damnation on all that is Jewish."

(Father András Kun, defrocked Minorite monk, 1945)

THE HALL OF THE ARROW CROSS

We enter an Arrow Cross assembly hall. The ghostly figure of Ferenc Szálasi stands at the head of the table. Informative photos of the Arrow Cross movement can be seen on the back wall. The monitors show contemporary filmed material, amongst them the deportation of Hungarian Jewry. Under the monitors Arrow Cross and SS uniforms are displayed. Loudspeakers blare sound clips from the program of the Hungarist Híradó (Hungarian Nazi Newsreel). Ice-floes drifting on the Danube projected onto the wall at the end of the hall conjure up the memory of Jewish vcitims shot on the Danube embankment in the winter of 1944-45.

Debrecen and Szeged were already in Soviet hands, fighting was going on East of the River Tisza, when on October 15 the Nazis delivered power into the hands of the Arrow Cross. The principal aim of Szálasi as "National Leader" was the total mobilization of Hungary's resources and manpower, as he was convinced that the miracle weapons promised by Hitler would transform the balance of power to Germany's advantage. Owing to its social program, anti-Semitic and nationalist demagoguery, as well as its radicalism, Szálasi's Hungarist movement had grown into a significant political force after the introduction of the secret ballot. Without German help and support, however, it could never have become a potential governing factor. After the October putsch, the range of Szálasi's "Hungarist state" was limited to Budapest and Transdanubia because of the Red Army's fast advance.

After the Arrow Cross take-over, the hitherto almost intact Budapest Jewish community of more than two-hundred thousand, was faced with the gravest peril. Adolf Eichmann, who had directed the deportation of provincial Jewry and who, after Regent Horthy had stopped the process in July, was forced to leave, now returned to Budapest on October 17. On Eichmann's instigation more than sixty thousand people were cruelly force-marched to the West to dig trenches on the Austrian border. About seventy-thousand of those remaining in the capital were locked into a ghetto. More than thirty thousand of the persecuted in possession of passes (Schutzpasses) issued by neutral countries sought refuge in so-called protected houses. The Arrow Cross militia raved and raged until the very last, shooting into the Danube Jews whom they wanted to loot, but the ghetto – the last one in Europe, but also the most fortunate – weathered the storm.

Prior to the Russians' total blockade of Budapest, the Arrow Cross administration, together with the "National Leader", relocated to Transdanubia, thence to the western borderlands. The German and Hungarian armies defended Budapest like a fortress; consequently the Soviet Army could take the capital only after prolonged and bitter fighting. The siege, lasting from Christmas 1944 to February 13, 1945, caused untold devastation and suffering. The Germans blew up all the bridges, public buildings were badly damaged, about thirty thousand residential ones were destroyed and became uninhabitable.

In March 1945 the Germans launched a last counter-attack against the Soviets near Lake Balaton, but by April the Red Army managed to push the last Nazis out of Hungary. Szálasi and his closest collaborators had already left the country by the end of March. More than a million people fled to the West ahead of the Red Army, more than a hundred thousand of them never to return. The total mobilization ordered by the Arrow Cross and the frenzied terror of the Arrow Cross thugs swelled the number of the war's victims by tens of thousands.

USZT-NYERA
SZUSZMAN
JARODNOJE
ZIRJANKA
JELGEN
KOLIMA

"In the Soviet Union work is a matter of honour and glory, of heroism and valiance!"

(Inscription over a camp gate)

The hall conjures up Soviet forced-labour and slave camps. Camp centres, where Hungarians languished, are specially marked on the carpet-map. The monitors show reminiscences, contemporary photographs, as well as pictures of the desolate, inhospitable Russian and Siberian countryside. The display cases contain relics, the original paraphernalia used by the detainees.

Everything that happened to the Hungarian prisoners fitted in with the ethnic cleansing, internment and forced labour-acquisition campaigns initiated in the twenties by internal squads in the Soviet Union's mainly non-Russian frontier zones, and continued during the war in Eastern Europe.
The abduction of Hungary's populace took place in two waves. After occupying a larger community, the Soviet forces would put the civilian population to work, but the "malenki robot" (little work) stipulated by the Soviet soldiers turned out to mean years of forced labour for many a luckless person. According to sporadic records, approximately three hundred people were taken from Hajdúböszörmény, six hundred from Balmazújváros, two thousand from Nyíregyháza, fifteen hundred from the region back of the River Tisza, a thousand civilians from the Hungarian side of the Bodrogköz. The number of civilians carried off from Budapest alone adds up to at least fifty thousand.
The second wave of abductions came about as a result of a resolution arrived at on December 16, 1944 by the Soviet Union's central organ, the State Defence Committee. The resolution pronounced the "mobilization" of able-bodied German nationals, but it affected the whole of Hungarian society. We are able to gather from available documents that the local Soviet authorities had to take a certain number of prisoners. Thus in those areas where there were no German residents, they picked up people with German-sounding names and eventually those with Hungarian names. In order to fill the quota, they often "mobilized" adolescents under 18 and even men over sixty. There were mass deportations in Sub-Carpathia, in Transylvania, and the eastern part of Slovakia, then under Hungarian rule. Political considerations also played an important part in the abductions. Soviet state security organs sought out and removed everyone whom they regarded as potentially dangerous for a communist takeover. That is how former political leaders, cabinet ministers, members of parliament, ambassadors, army officers, priests and schoolteachers ended up in Soviet prisons and forced labour camps. Raoul Wallenberg, the Swedish diplomat, who had saved the lives of thousands of Jews, was captured and taken to the Soviet Union. According to Hungarian and Soviet documents, some 130-180 thousand civilians were captured and deported from the area of today's Hungary. Together with the soldiers – most of whom were "taken prisoner" after the cessation of hostilities in Europe – altogether 600-700 thousand former Hungarian citizens ended up in Soviet captivity.
Hungarian citizens abducted for "malenki robot" were first taken to reception centres in Hungary, thence to transit camps at Máramarossziget, Foksányi, Brassó and Temesvár respectively. Terrible conditions prevailed in these camps and many of the prisoners succumbed to their wretched existence. Those who survived were then transported in cattle trucks to one or the other of the thousands of remote camps that made up the huge Soviet gulag.

The system of Soviet concentration and labour camps was organized in 1919 with the aim of segregating, punishing and utilizing the labour of all those, whom the Soviet regime regarded as its enemies. "GULAG" actually stands for the central administration of the camps, but in common parlance the term is used for Soviet concentration camps in general.
Many millions of people perished over the decades in the camps of the gulag. There were years when, due to the guards' brutality, the quota of executions ordered by the Soviet authorities, the inhuman conditions, the 10-12 hours of strenuous work, starvation and freezing weather, the number of victims amounted to several million. The prisoners worked in mines, on road-, dam- and railway-constructions under appalling conditions without adequate tools, rations and clothing. The Hungarian prisoners, similarly to other foreign prisoners, were placed into camps under the direction of the "Inspectorate of Prisoners-of-War and Internees" (GUPVI). This system was the foreigners' "gulag". The Soviet authorities had established GUPVI in 1939, at the very beginning of World War II. The war served as a good opportunity for the Soviet Union to replenish its diminishing manpower reserves by forced labourers imported from the territories occupied by the Red Army. The Hungarian prisoners were dispersed in over a thousand different camps. In the course of their transportation, as well as due to the miserable working and living conditions, a total of some 300 thousand Hungarian forced labourers lost their lives. Soviet military courts sentenced several thousand Hungarian citizens to death or long prison terms, in Soviet parlance: "corrective forced labour". In the case of those to be executed there was no investigation, no direction for evidence, only the verdict that was carried out without delay. Survivors were able to leave the Soviet Union during the early fifties. Many of them, however, were not allowed to return to their families even after the expiration of their punishment. At the Hungarian border they were intercepted by the ÁVH; some of them were interned, others were allowed to proceed home, but the latter were bound to secrecy. They had to remain silent until the change of regime.
The last Hungarian prisoner-of-war, András Toma, returned home from Russia in the year 2000.

"Unfortunately, now and then fascists do manage to slip into our Party."

(Mátyás Rákosi, 1945)

CHANGEROOM

The hall symbolizes the continuity of the dictatorships, as well as denoting that all strata of society "changed their clothes", entering into a totally different world. There are authentic telephones in two of the fitting rooms. On one of them one can hear the reminiscences of György Faludy, the famous poet, on the other contemporary jokes. The picture sequences visible on the screen demonstrate how the entire country changed from one warped regime to a new, just as warped, inhumane regime.

In the 1939 parliamentary elections the Arrow Cross became the second strongest party. It had more than three hundred thousand members. The Hungarian national socialists were supported by an electorate numbering close to a million. They received every third vote in the working-class districts of Budapest.

The Communist Party, operating in illegality since 1919, consisted of a mere few hundred members in the period preceding Soviet occupation. When, in the wake of the Red Army, the Communist Party of Hungary (MKP) began to reorganize, the increase of its membership became a vital necessity. Since members of the Party managed straight after the war to take hold of the investigative organs of the Interior and of the Political Sections of the Department of Defence, they could also put their hands on the Arrow Cross membership records. Subsequently there was a rush to join the Communist Party by certain elements that – as Mátyás Rákosi conceded – "had been to a greater or lesser degree influenced by the counter-revolution and the corrupting effect of fascism." The "small-time Arrow Cross followers", who were admitted to the Communist Party, had to declare when and for how long they had been members, and whether they now regarded their membership as a mistake which they wanted to put right. These declarations were, without any doubt, suitable for frightening and blackmailing the signatories. At a later stage the Communist Party made an effort to rid itself of members with such doubtful pasts.

"Each and every one of our decrees was a blow to the secret plans of the American imperialists, to Tito and his Hungarian hirelings."

(Mátyás Rákosi, 1949)

THE FIFTIES

The hall puts on view the darkest period of communism in Hungary. The monitors show newsreel clips from the fifties. Through the headphones we can hear archival recordings of political speeches by communist leaders of the era. Behind the backdrop one can see secret listening devices; social-realist paintings decorate the walls. We have placed the personal documents of ÁVH leaders and some instruments of torture in the glass cabinets.

By the spring of 1945 the Red Army had driven out the Nazis from Hungary. Wartime losses were horrific. Ten percent of the population had perished, the country was in ruins. Everyday life had to be re-established. Significant portions of the forces advocating a bourgeois democracy gathered round the Independent Smallholder, the National Peasant and the Bourgeois Democratic Party. The Soviet occupying forces and the Allied Control Commission, which until the peace treaty was in de facto charge of the country and operated under the direction of Marshall Voroshilov, supported a soviet-type reconstruction and the Communist Party. The majority of the Hungarian people, however, wanted to live in a democracy. At the general elections of 1945 57% voted for the Smallholders Party and barely 17% for the communists. Despite this electoral victory the Allied Control Commission did not sanction the formation of a purely bourgeois government. It also stipulated that the Ministry of the Interior and the Political Police be under communist control. With the help of the latter the communists deployed every means, including assassinations and terrorizing the populace, in their effort to seize total power. Eventually in 1947 the Communist Party openly introduced a totalitarian dictatorship. Terror and intimidation now became the daily routine. The decisive move which dealt the death-blow to the budding democracy was the arrest and abduction on February 25 by Soviet security police of the deposed Secretary-General of the Smallholders' Party, the deputy Béla Kovács. Soon thereafter Prime Minister Ferenc Nagy was ousted in a putsch and parliament suspended. The Communist Party under the leadership of Interior Minister László Rajk, managed to gain 22% in the hastily called elections. This was the infamous "blue ticket" election, during the course of which hundreds of thousands were disenfranchised, and some two hundred thousand fake, blue ticket votes were cast. Another approximately seven hundred thousand voting papers were destroyed to facilitate the Leftist Bloc's aspiration finally to form a government. Leaders of the opposition were forced to go abroad or imprisoned. The merger of the MKP and the Social Democratic Party resulted in the formation of a new, united Hungarian Workers' Party (MDP), sounding the death-knell of the old-established Social Democrats. Shortly thereafter the former leaders of the Social Democratic Party were imprisoned. Private ownership was abolished step by step. Industry, education, financial and commercial services, cultural institutions were nationalized. By the spring of 1949, electors could vote only for the party-state's nominees: members of the MDP, and reliable non-party "fellow-travellers". 220,000 so-called "peoples' educators" were deployed to augment the voters' waning enthusiasm. The ÁVH was also a considerable help. The result: a 96% electoral victory. The first free elections had to wait until 1990.

”MAGYARORSZÁG
A BÉKE
SZAVAZÓ
URNA

"Vigilance is an indispensable communist attribute."

(Szabad Nép, 1951)

WORKADAY COMMUNISM

In countries, where the Red Army had ejected the Nazi occupiers, the Soviet Union imposed a socialist type of societal arrangement.

The iron curtain descended, borders were hermetically closed, mined; one could no longer get away from the socialist countries. Those who nonetheless tried to, had to reckon with at best long prison sentences, but there were some who met their death on the minefields, others were shot while escaping or captured and executed. The Soviets were the ones who appointed the leaders in the "fraternal" socialist countries, who in turn raised the Communist Parties to power.

In Hungary the political parties were abolished, a one-party system introduced, although this was never expressly laid down by law. Most social organizations and societies were banned. Only followers of the Hungarian Workers' Party enjoyed political representation. Every idea, theory, view, that did not conform to the party-line was regarded as hostile and to be eradicated. The Party's ideology, which they called Marxism-Leninism and Stalinism respectively, spread its tentacles over the economy, cultural life, education and daily life.

Parliamentary government ceased to exist, as did political debates. Organs of the state were controlled by party bodies; real decision-making was in the hands of the party leadership, that is, the Political Committee. Mátyás Rákosi, "our father", "our wise leader", "Stalin's foremost Hungarian pupil", stood at the head of the Party. But every level had its own leader, its own "local kinglet", as the party secretaries were referred to at the time.

Military discipline ruled in the party-state, and it progressively extended over the whole of society. Daily life became militarized; the entire country was gripped by war-psychosis.

The communists changed the constitution; they declared Hungary a People's Republic. This, according to their view, brought the country a step closer to their aim: socialism.

Instead of local organs of self-government, they instituted a system of councils on the Soviet pattern. They abolished private ownership and took over control of the trade unions. They introduced a centralized, planned economy, which soon bankrupted the country. Shortages became a permanent economic feature; shelves in the shops were empty. People had to queue up for hours; bread and sugar were for a long time available only with food coupons. All this did not affect the party leadership – the "functionaries" as they were called. They received special treatment. Everything became politicized: party soldiers were put into leading economic positions who, although "ideologically developed", had not an inkling of economic matters.

The Party initiated ideological training already at kindergarten level. Children progressed from there to "little drummer boys", thence to the "pioneers" and finally to the DISZ, a "democratic" student organization. Of course, only if the child was of a suitable background, i.e. not a class-alien or religious, its parents were not interned, resettled, or in prison. Such a background was a grave disadvantage for admission to tertiary education or getting work.

On the job and after hours one had to continually affirm belief in the regime. Before the beginning of the working day, during the so-called "Szabad Nép half-hours", the communal reading of the Party's official organ, it was mandatory to intensify one's ideological bonding. For the same reason one had to participate in seminaria, socialist work-competitions, and on the weekends in "voluntary" solidarity shifts. The latter was the "Communist Saturday". Similarly, one could "volunteer" to subscribe to the Peace Loan. They changed the Hungarian coat-of-arms.

At official functions they made us sing the Soviet anthem and 'The Internationale' instead of the Hungarian national anthem. Hungarian national holidays, such as the 15th of March, were declared workdays. In their stead the country was made to celebrate April 4, the "Day of Liberation" and November 7, the day of the Bolshevik take-over. Those who did not show sufficient enthusiasm were promptly denounced by the ubiquitous informers. People learned to whisper; they were in constant fear of their conversations being intercepted.
Terror cast its shadow over daily life.

"Hungary must be punished in an exemplary fashion."

(Stalin, 1946)

SOVIET ADVISORS

For a long time after 1945, Soviet advisors operating alongside Hungarian political, social and economic leaders endeavoured to force their own methods and lifestyle on to Hungarian society. Documentaries and newsreel clips shown on the monitors in the hall evoke the Soviet presence.

The first Soviet advisors appeared on Hungarian soil in 1944, almost simultaneously with the advancing Red Army. The majority was political officers or worked for military intelligence. Their task was to establish a new Hungarian administration, which would willingly cooperate with the Soviet occupying authorities. Parties and social organizations could not operate without their consent, nor could the press, and mass rallies needed their permission. They were the ones who determined the number of Hungarian and German-speaking people to be deported to the Soviet Union.
After the expulsion of the Nazis, Hungary's political and economic life was placed under the supervision of the Soviet-led Allied Control Commission (SZEB). Marshal Voroshilov was head of SZEB, followed by Lieutenant-General Sviridov. After the cessation of the SZEB (September 15, 1947), the incumbent Soviet ambassadors became the Kremlin's Hungarian "regents". Ambassadors Pushkin, Tyiskov, Kiseliov and Andropov were at the same time high-ranking members of the Soviet political police. The Soviet advisors kept an all-encompassing filing system of the communist leadership, opposition politicians, the intelligentsia, Hungarian public personages. For them even Rákosi, who danced attendance on Moscow, was not reliable enough.
Soviet advisors "helped" the Political Police, and later the ÁVO, thence the ÁVH, the KATPOL (Military-Political Department) and the GRO (Economic Police) in all their more significant investigative and evaluation work. Their presence at important interrogations assured "impartial expertise". Arrests were carried out, political trials organized on the Soviet model with their efficient collaboration. General Belkin, who directed the Central European countries' political police organs from Baden near Vienna, frequently visited Budapest in order personally to make sure that the advisors carried out their work in a satisfactory manner. The ministries and judicial authorities too could rely on the Soviet advisors. Soviet experts were the long-term economic decision-makers in Hungary. They directed uranium mining, air transport, the munitions and oil industries. They supervised foreign trade and all the strategic branches of the economy. The Hungarian army was also moulded according to the Soviet model.
The aim of Soviet educators, engineers, doctors, agriculturalists, miners visiting Hungary was not only to convey the experiences of the "advanced Soviet industry and agriculture" to their Hungarian colleagues, but to try and make them accept a lifestyle and a mentality totally alien to the Hungarian people. The ever-growing Soviet colony was under the supervision of the Soviet embassy in Budapest and the Soviet political police. The sight of Soviet soldiers stationed in our fatherland became part and parcel of the Hungarian countryside. Their network of garrisons was spread all over the state. Together with Ambassador Andropov, the Soviet advisors took the lion's share in preparing the Soviet intervention of 1956. The Soviet tanks entering revolutionary Budapest, which transported János Kádár and some members of his government to the building of the Hungarian Parliament, also carried Kádár's two personal advisors, Baikov and Kupchenko. The two of them, who remained in his close proximity until the spring of 1957, did not leave him out of sight even during the night. They

slept in a room adjoining Kádár's, and they were his interpreters during his telephone conversations with Khrushchev. Three high-ranking Soviet officials: Malenkov, Suslov and Aristov, spent part of the autumn of 1956 in Budapest in order to supervise the Kádár government's initial performance and to direct reprisals from behind the scenes. The last Soviet advisors left Hungary in 1989.

23
ДА ЗДРАВСТВУЕТ ДРУЖБА
СОВЕТСКОГО-ВЕНГЕРСКОГО
НАРОДА!

JELENTÉSE ANNAK, HOGY VOLT ELLENÁLLÁS, HOGY NEM FEKÜDT LE

"Because the people said: enough!"

(Sándor Márai)

RESISTANCE

Following World War II, the communists forced a new ideological-political system on Hungary. In reply resistance movements were organized in our fatherland with the participation of representatives from all social strata. The three monitors in the hall display the reminiscences of survivors, who took part in the resistance movements of 1945-1956. Copies of contemporary propaganda leaflets can be seen on the tables.

The Soviet occupiers set up a "new world order" in Hungary, in which there was no place for old values, old virtues. It was a Soviet world, fit for Soviet-type people, but alien and unacceptable to the majority of Hungarians.
They persecuted religion. Instead of God, the Party's leaders Stalin and Rákosi had to be venerated. Patriotism was prohibited. They demanded that Hungarians identify with the aims and interests of the Soviet Union. They turned family members and the different generations against each other. It became compulsory to inform against one's family. Pavlik Morozov, the Soviet child who denounced his own kulak father for "sabotage", was set up as the quintessential model. Those who were not willing to accept this had to face the all-encompassing, ever-present terror machine, the ÁVO. The regime was built on terror and threats.
A country-wide resistance movement, extending over all social strata, emerged in response to the communist dictatorship. There were but few corners of the country without larger or smaller such resistance groups. Tens of thousands were prepared to undertake armed resistance, print and distribute leaflets, get in touch with representatives of the Western powers, carry out acts of sabotage or any other form of resistance. Many of them risked their lives. Some collected weapons left over from the war, ready to fight for freedom when the occasion arose. The death penalty or life-imprisonment was to be their lot. In barely more than ten years (between 1945 and 1956) some fifteen hundred persons in more than fifty cases were brought before the courts accused of sedition. Close on four hundred of them were executed: students organizing acts of sabotage all over the country, peasants, who refused compulsory delivery of produce. They imprisoned 15-16 year old children who painted *"Hang Rákosi!"* and *"Death to the Communists!"* on the sidewalk in Balatonfűzfő.
In Békéssámson the Hungarian Resistance Movement operated for over four years. They distributed their famous leaflets – *"The Hungarian Plains weep, under the crush of Russian feet"* and *"We're watching you, ÁVO squealer!"* – all over the country. There were more than twenty of them. Two of them were sentenced to death, others to long prison terms. At Farkasfa, the smallest village in Vas county and in the surrounds, the ÁVO apprehended 80 people for helping illegal border-crossers. Two of them were beaten to death during interrogation, seven – amongst them a woman – were executed, the others received long prison sentences. The "Ragged Gang" (28 accused), the "Anti-Bolshevik Hungarian Resistance Movement" (19 accused), the "Zala White Guards" (86 accused), the "Sword and Cross Movement" (28 accused), the Pálosszentkút, Kesztölc and Baja resistance groups (76 accused), the military resistance movement, the Fraternal Collective of Hungarian Fighters (36 accused), the case of Colonel Pál Hadváry (5 accused) – are but examples picked out at random. That is to say, in all parts of the country, in each generation, every social stratum, resistance was rife. Students, whose schools were abolished, whose

teachers were resettled or arrested, whose parents were intimidated, became resisters; army officers, who could not resign themselves to Hungary becoming a Soviet satellite; workers, who were defending their rights they had fought for; peasants, whose lives were being made miserable by kulak lists, impossible compulsory delivery demands, house-searches; teachers, lawyers, doctors, who did not put up with the erosion of their political rights. Because they would not suffer the humiliation, because they did not wish to live in fear. They wanted an independent, democratic Hungary.

Communism turned almost everybody against itself. It sufficed to miss out on one Szabad Nép half-hour, to tell a joke, to show too little enthusiasm, or give money to the families of "social outcasts", or even just to nod to them. Anyone, who did not applaud loud enough, came under suspicion.

The brave ones, who defied the atrocious terror regime, were wiped out and buried in unmarked graves, because even in death they represented a threat. The oppressive system did everything in its power to eradicate even their memories. Those, who risked their lives for the freedom of their country, were branded spies and traitors. We do not know the names of many of them, and old lies still keep circulating about some of them. Yet they were true heroes.

"Out with the idlers, they pollute the air of Budapest!"

(Lajos Kónya, 1952)

RESETTLEMENT AND DEPORTATION

In the spring and summer of 1944, hundreds of thousands were deported from Hungary. The tragedy of the Jews was followed by the local German population's tragedy. Between 1946 and 1948, some two hundred thousand ethnic Germans were expelled and resettled in occupied Germany. Subsequently more than ten thousand country dwellers were transported to so-called "closed" – in reality concentration – camps, where the guards were not held accountable for the prisoners' lives. In 1951, thousands of the capitals' middle, - upper-middle class and titled citizens were forcibly transferred to designated quarters in the countryside. It is their fate that is illustrated in the hall by way of photographs and documents. The ZIM automobile on display is a frightening relic of the times: it evokes the infamous "black car" used by the communist political police to pick up its victims. Millions were in dread of these nocturnal visitors, and the ringing of the bell that heralded their arrival. That is when the expression: "bell-panic" was coined.

The era of collective persecution did not end with the war. As part of the Potsdam Declaration, issued in June 1945, the victorious Allied Powers authorized the expulsion of the ethnic Germans from Eastern Europe. Hungary, too, was authorized to get rid of some of its Germans. Originally, only such Germans were to be deported who had belonged to the Volksbund, a pro-Nazi ethnic organization; in reality, mainly those were sent to Germany, a total of about 200,000, whose houses and lands were worth expropriating. The humiliated, dispossessed citizens of German origin were transported under inhuman conditions to Germany. After the loss in human life due to the war, the annihilation of the bulk of our Jewish fellow-citizens and the hundreds of thousands deported to the Soviet Union, the expulsion of yet another close to quarter of a million Hungarian citizens caused irreparable harm.

Czechoslovakia, one of the victors, also endeavoured to get rid of its German and Hungarian minorities. The latter's oppression took place in a manner, which, in its hypocrisy, surpassed many other persecutions in an age when ethnic persecution, and deportation were everyday affairs. Under the auspices of the infamous Benes Decrees, members of the Magyar minority were forced to wear a distinguishing "M" mark. The aim was unilaterally to expel two hundred thousand Hungarians. Eventually under the Hungarian-Czechoslovak population exchange agreement of 1946, more than one hundred thousand Hungarians were forced to leave their homeland where their roots had been since time immemorial, while close to sixty thousand Slovaks were resettled from Hungary. (This was called "Re-Slovakization".)

First in 1951 and then in the summer of 1952 part of the inhabitants of the Yugoslav-Hungarian border region were resettled. These so-called "unreliables" were often taken away at night to compulsory quarters in remote parts of the country or confined to labour camps. The former were divested of their civic rights, lost their pensions, were forbidden to leave their addresses without permission, had to leave behind their goods and chattels and were placed under twenty-four hour supervision. The summer of 1951 saw the mass forced evacuations from Budapest, Győr, Szombathely and Székesfehérvár. In a large-scale and well-prepared action, lasting from May 21 to July 18, more than five thousand families, some fifteen thousand persons, were removed from the capital. They were allowed to take goods weighing no more than 250 kilos. The rest of

their belongings were inventoried in triplicate. The more valuable pieces, such as furniture, were appropriated by "party cadres" moving into larger apartments. The rest became state property. The most hard-hit of the forced evacuees were those who were confined to so-called "social camps" – enclosed agricultural forced-labour camps, surrounded by barbed wire, guarded by ÁVO soldiers and dogs. They were housed in sheep-pens or barracks and were put to work under terrible conditions. Working days lasted 12 hours. The distance to the workplaces was usually 8-10 kilometres from their base, which the forced-labourers had to make to and fro on foot each day. Many died or suffered lasting health problems through insufficient nourishment, harsh conditions, strenuous labour and lack of medical facilities. Between June 1950 and October 1953 some fifteen thousand people were made to work in the forced-labour camps of the Hortobágy region.
Use of the term "deportation" was officially prohibited, and whosoever committed a slip of the tongue or the pen, was punished. The forcibly evacuated were chosen for their social origins, but filthy lucre also played a part. After all, it was the fastest and simplest way to acquire fine houses and apartments for the Party's "upwardly mobile" cadres. Some of the forced evacuees had lived through the horrors of Nazi concentration camps. The prospect of yet another deportation caused a number of them to commit suicide, yet others dug up their yellow stars and pinned them on once again.
"Class-aliens" of military age, who were automatically considered unreliable, were called up for labour service. They were put to work on construction sites and mines in the country's most god-forsaken areas.
In June 1953 Imre Nagy's government rescinded the expulsion regulations, but the majority of forced evacuees could never return to their original homes. Nor did adverse discrimination die down against those who had returned.

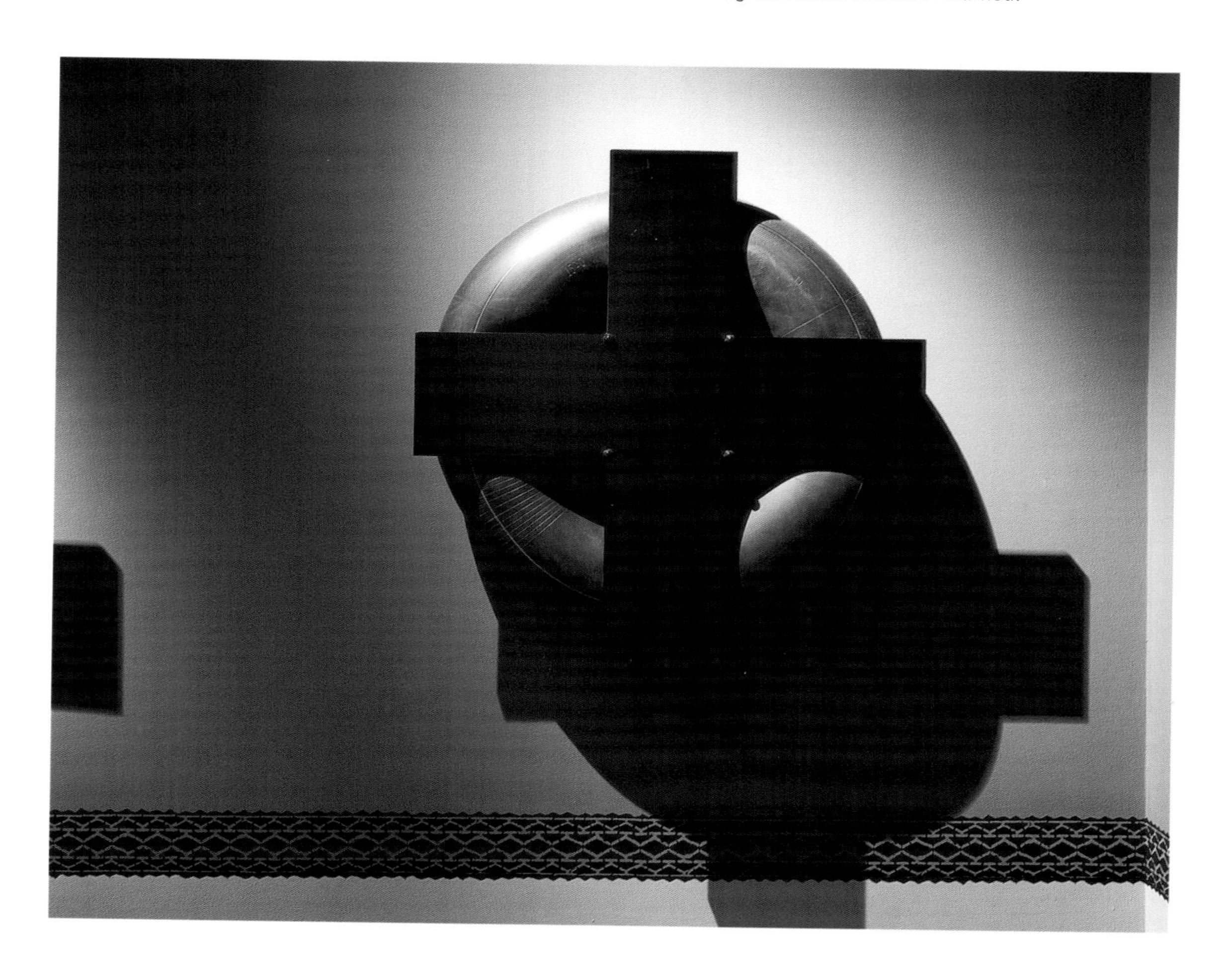

"One must strike with all possible means..."

(János Kádár, 1949)

THE TORTURE CHAMBER

This room was preserved in its original form. At the time, it was referred to as the gym. On the wall we can see special instruments of torture: a knout with nails, a lead-headed bamboo stick, an Arrow Cross truncheon, a club covered in leather with a lead spring.

"I was taken directly to 60 Andrássy Road. My first interrogation lasted all of 18 hours.
I never imagined that a 56-year-old man could be so severely beaten, kicked, tortured with all sorts of instruments, drugged by injections that he could be deprived of his will-power. They gave me the third degree with high-voltage current, with electric shocks. I had to stand on tiptoes on a plank studded with nails and flanked by red-hot hotplates to make me stand erect. I collapsed. I realized that they did not want to make a martyr of me, but to turn me into a despicable man. After 18 hours of such questioning they handed me to an ÁVO jailer, who led me to the basement prison of 60 Andrássy Road. They stripped me on the ice-cold flagstones. There was only one bunk in the cell and it was thick with dirt. For the first two months they never even gave me a blanket. A light was burning all night. One could only infer from the street noise whether it was night or day. There was a spy hole in the cell door, and the guard kept peering in periodically. I had to sit on the bunk without leaning against the wall.
I was taken to an elegant room for interrogation, where I was stripped naked and made to perform gymnastics, up-and-down, in front of a young ÁVO man; each time I would bend down, I had to kiss his feet until I finally collapsed.
Subsequently I spent about two weeks in the subterranean prison's punishment cell. It was a 2 x 1.3 metre crypt-like cubicle with the ubiquitous bunk. Deep below the ground, so much so that the sewer pipe was above the bunk, and kept dripping disgustingly. There was only a tiny section of the bunk, where I dared to sit down. During the two weeks I never laid down. Now and then during the day I fell asleep totally exhausted, sitting erect without leaning against the wall. They did not give me a blanket. It was November. I was freezing. My primary prayer in those ghastly days was: Would that I could meet my Maker, lest I hurt someone with my confession...
Sometimes they led me to the lieutenant-colonel. He sat at the head of his large desk, I on the opposite end. 5-6 men in mufti sat around me in chairs. Three on the leather settee, an ÁVO major and two captains. The detectives then spat in my face and in my eyes. To the lieutenant-colonel's question, whether they could suggest anything else to break my will apart from torture, the three ÁVO men settled on torture. They then dragged me to the same room where I had been a fortnight earlier, and the same three men: a hulking major, an average-sized first lieutenant or captain and a civilian of medium height, surrounded me. Once again they stripped me naked, and made me work out until I dropped. All the while they clobbered me from the back, mainly under the nape of my neck, between my shoulder blades, with some sort of flat object, because it did not swell up; I could not move my head though for two or three days. They kept kicking my spine. The forced gymnastics took several forms. Facing the wall, they placed a pencil-like metal object between my forehead and the wall, while I had to stand on tiptoes, upturned spikes and nails beneath my heels to make me stand still. I was flanked by two burning hotplates. All my insides were tense, and I couldn't move any part of my body. When I collapsed, they pulled out the studded plank from underneath me, and stood me upright with a few kicks. Another method was to make me squat. I had to crouch with 10-15 kilo weights in my hands over barbed spikes until I collapsed. Then they once again heaved me upright with blows and kicks. Yet another method was the use of electric shocks. As far as I can judge, each torture session lasted for about an hour. By morning there were palm-sized abscesses on both my knees."
Vendel Endrédy, abbot of Zirc (arrested in 1950).

„A GAZDASÁGI ÉLET
EGYIK LEGNAGYOBB PROBLÉMÁJA
A DISZNÓKÉRDÉS. EZZEL KAPCSOLATBAN
AZ A HELYZET, HOGY A DISZNÓK JELENLEG
A KULÁKSÁG KEZÉBEN VANNAK.
A GABONAFRONTON SIKERÜLT MEGVERNI
A KULÁKOKAT ÉS EZÉRT AZOK
MOST A ZSÍRELLÁTÁS ALAPJÁT KÉPEZŐ DISZNÓK
KISAJÁTÍTÁSÁVAL AKARNAK ÜTNI
A DEMOKRÁCIÁN."
KÁDÁR JÁNOS
1 kg
SERTÉSZSÍR

"The ÁVH looks after the labouring peasantry as well."

(Szabad Nép, 1950)

COMPULSORY DELIVERIES

The hall shows the period when the peasantry was forced to hand over a fixed quota of its surplus agricultural produce and livestock to state organs at fixed prices. The monitors display contemporary propaganda films about the fulfilment of the delivery obligations and about socialist work competitions. Former so-called kulaks talk about the atrocities, the commandeerings, the so-called "attic sweepings", the humiliations. We have placed contemporary documents on the walls, regulating the peasants' obligations, food coupons, and the slaughter of animals. The "white piglet" symbolizes under the counter slaughters.

After the horrible devastation caused by World War II, the Hungarian peasantry looked forward to a brighter future. Hundreds of thousands came into possession of land by way of the 1945 land redistribution. The old and the happy new owners were confident that their livelihood was now secure. Wartime restrictions did not, however, cease at the same time as did the din of battle. Farmers had to continue to fulfil their obligation of handing over their compulsory quota; only then were they permitted to dispose freely of their produce. The reason for that was that the Hungarian peasantry had to take care not only of the populace's and the occupying Soviet army's provisions, but had to produce foodstuff for reparations as well. Produce was divided into three portions: one part remained the property of the farmer and his family; another was kept for sowing seed to assure next year's crop, and the third had to be handed in. Simultaneously with their seizure of power, the communists initiated a ruthless campaign against the Hungarian peasantry. Between 1948 and 1953 they tripled the farmers' obligations. In 1952 they also changed the sequence. First the peasants had to hand over the compulsory amount, and only then came the turn of the sowing seed and the family's own quota. If and when enough was left over. Then came the so-called "attic sweepings". The official collectors used to arrive with ÁVH-men, scaring the wits out of the whole village.

The Party did not spare any efforts in its aim to destroy the countryside's traditional lifestyle and to force the peasants to abandon their lands. This policy served a dual purpose. In its preparation for a third world war the Soviet Union and its satellites, thus Hungary too, had to make significant investments as far as heavy industry was concerned. A considerable part of these investments was covered by the exploitation of agriculture. That was one reason why they commandeered everything from the peasantry, and also because they needed a workforce for their heavy industry. And in any case, the communist system could not abide the continued existence of an economically independent community carrying on its traditional lifestyle. The elimination of a land-owning Hungarian peasantry wedded to its conservative values, customs and traditions, was indispensable for the party-state in order to extend its dictatorship over the entire country.

The focus of attacks was the "kulak" on the Soviet model. The term kulak has no equivalent in the Hungarian language. They did not even try to translate it. Anyone could become a kulak, i.e. a public enemy, the hunters' prey. Kulak lists were prepared and the villages' most eminent and most successful farmers were put on these lists. In principle a kulak had to own at least 13 hectares, in practice though it was left to the judgement of the local party functionaries to decide whom they regarded as such. They were continuously harassed with special taxes, increased compulsory quotas, by means of physical

and psychological bullying. Kulak-beating brigades frequented the villages to keep the inhabitants under their thumb by public punitive actions, by thrashings. They tried to break the people's spirits by forced-labour, forced evacuations, confiscations of property, hundreds of thousands of trumped-up charges, thousands of court cases, long prison terms and executions. Four hundred thousand peasants were convicted for "public supply crimes" alone. Resistance was so strong that "public enemies" were arrested by the score in some villages. Many of them lost their lives.
It is little wonder then that in the 1950s three hundred thousand peasants left their land. Ten percent of the country's arable land remained uncultivated. Those peasants who stayed on also lost their enthusiasm for farming. Huge food shortages were the result of all this. Rationing had to be introduced once again and the "saboteurs" exposed. That is to say, scapegoats had to be found, because in the socialist system, sabotage by the yet to be uncovered enemy served as a blanket explanation for every fiasco. The search for scapegoats was therefore arranged. One court case after another with severe sentences was brought against farmers. They spread lies that the managers of the Meat Marketing Organization were responsible for the meat shortage. They were executed. "Threshing sabotage" drew the death penalty; "under the counter" slaughtering of animals was punished by severe prison sentences. On top of everything, the "decades-long experience of the vanguard Soviet agriculture" was forced on to the Hungarian countryside, a model which even after several decades had not managed to avert the necessity of imports, although Russia used to produce a significant superabundance of grain. Following the experiences of the "vanguard", a centrally directed planned agriculture was introduced in Hungary, and individual farmers were told where, what and when to produce. One such memorable botched attempt was the forced rice and cotton production.
After the abolition of individual farms they tried to drive the Hungarian peasantry into state-controlled kolkhozes on the Soviet model. This attempt, however, for the time being at least – until the 60s – failed under the Hungarian peasantry's resistance.

1 kg
SERTÉSZSÍR
1 kg
SERTÉSZSÍR
1 kg
SERTÉSZSÍR
1 kg
SERTÉSZSÍR
1 kg
SERTÉSZSÍR
1 kg
SERTÉSZSÍR
1 kg
SERTÉSZSÍR
1 kg
SERTÉSZSÍR

"The ÁVH's investigators and workers stem from the people, and love the labouring masses with all their heart."

(Szabad Nép, 1950)

ÁVO ENTRANCE HALL

The group photo on the wall presents a number of members of the Communist Political Police's (PRO, ÁVO, and ÁVH) chiefs-of-staff. Propaganda film clips can be observed on the monitors. The bench situated in the centre of the hall symbolizes communist monuments.
"... It is not by accident that we have requisitioned the building in 60 Andrássy Road for the PRO. We, who have lived here, know that the events of 1944 had their origins primarily in 60 Andrássy Road, and everything that happened after October 15, 1944 emanated from here. ... The guilty parties should receive their just deserts in the building whence they have set out..." (Gábor Péter, 1947).

The siege of Buda was still in full swing, when on January 17, 1945 the Political Security Department was established on the Soviet model, led by Gábor Péter, a primary school dropout and a former journeyman tailor, who had never actually pursued his craft. The official purpose of the soon-to-become infamous and dreaded organization was the ferreting out and indictment of war criminals. In addition the organization, initially made up of ex-labour service men, far-left elements, criminals and a great number of former Arrow Cross henchmen, was given the task by the Communist Party to obstruct the development of constitutionalism, thereby preparing the ground for the Communist Party's take-over.
At first they wore dove grey and subsequently sand-coloured uniforms; later their service-caps bore a red star in a circlet of corn. The syllabus of the Soviet Political Police and the Dzerzhinsky Academy, established in Budapest on the Moscow model, inculcated the merciless hatred of the class-enemy in the PRO officers. The Hungarian Political Police – similarly to its prototype, the Cheka and its successors – became the communist dictatorship's support and only real guarantee. That is why it was called the "Fist of the Party".
In October 1946 the ÁVO, with Gábor Péter at its head, was born out of the merger of the PRO with the regional departments. Its headquarters remained in 60 Andrássy Road. One of the new organization's tasks was the eradication of the democratic political parties and the concomitant intelligence work. Its members and agents infiltrated each party, the Churches and spared no effort in trying to destroy Hungarian expatriate circles. The destruction of these communities was one of the most important of their political aims. They monitored correspondences and telephone conversations. Their network of informants and agents covered the country, infiltrated private homes. They kept records of, and spied on, millions of citizens whom they declared to be their political enemies. One month after he was appointed Minister of the Interior, János Kádár began in September 1948 to organize the ÁVH. This State Security organ, independent from the police and under the exclusive umbrella of the Hungarian Workers' Party, was established on December 28, 1949 under the leadership of Gábor Péter. Its jurisdiction was extended over the border and river police as well; this internal force specialized in terrorizing the entire country. The ÁVH gobbled up the notorious Military Political Department (KATPOL), which had come into being in the spring of 1945, and which had hitherto operated within the framework of the Ministry of Defence. However, only the names of the communist terror organizations changed over the years; their mission never did. No sphere of life was secure from them.

A MI
POLITIKAI NYOMOZÓINK
AZ ÁLLAMVÉDELMI HATÓSÁG
DOLGOZÓI,
A MAGYAR NÉP L
ÓL KERÜLNEK KI

"All honest men are filled with a sense of security and strength, when seeing ÁVO-officers."

(Szabad Nép, 1950)

GÁBOR PÉTER'S ROOM

We have recreated the erstwhile study of the ÁVH's chief on the basis of photographs and recollections. On the monitors surviving victims report on the interrogation methods of the ÁVH. The small screens show communists, who at first were the regime's leaders, later its prisoners and victims. Many of them were at first interrogators, then confessors, and subsequently joined the ranks of interrogators again.

The political police under Gábor Péter's leadership was essentially organized to carry out the Party's directives. In accordance with the interests of the incumbent Party boss and naurally of Moscow, they – if ordered to – arrested, tortured and for that matter, beat to death their parents, siblings, lovers, friends, former comrades-in-arms, and even comrades. When still Minister of the Interior, László Rajk frequently visited 60 Andrássy Road in order personally to supervise the ÁVO's work connected with his special cases. In 1949, however, it was he who found himself in crosshairs. His former subordinates forced him to make a confession. He was sentenced to death and executed, together with four of his co-defendants. Soon thereafter, almost two hundred labour activists fell into the ÁVH's clutches. Before long an increasing number of communist leaders, among them Rajk's successor, János Kádár – the erstwhile founder of the ÁVH – ended up in the torture chambers run by their colleagues. They were followed by the traitors of the democratic labour movement, the left-wing Social Democrats, who had delivered the Social Democratic Party into the hands of the communists in exchange for high positions. They too received lengthy prison sentences. From 1950 onwards, purges were carried out within the ranks of the Political Police as well. Ernő Szűcs, deputy head of the ÁVH, had his own younger brother tortured in the cellar prison; eventually Rákosi had both of them beaten to death. Even Gábor Péter could not avoid his fate. He and dozens of his colleagues ended up behind bars in January 1953 as a result of Stalin's anti-Semitic paranoia. Following the Prague trial of Slánsky, which concluded with the execution of the predominantly Jewish members of his party and government, the Soviet dictator gave orders that Zionist plots be "uncovered" in the socialist countries. His most faithful disciple, Mátyás Rákosi, did not hesitate to throw to the wolves the ÁVH's henchmen of Jewish origin, who had for years obediently carried out his inhumane orders. Numbers of Hungarian Jews, who stood up for their faith and for Israel, were also arrested at the same time. It was Stalin's death that averted the persecution of Jews in Hungary. Deprived of its right to schooling, further education, homes, travel, and professional recognition – that is how Hungarian society vegetated in the era of the ÁVH and its successor organization. They wanted to change the people into subjects in this regime of systematic terror, that is why they kept up the relentless pressure for compliance and subservience. The ÁVH, as such, did not survive the Revolution of 1956. After János Kádár came into power, however, he continued to rely on the several thousand-strong activist army, which in the wake of the Soviet onslaught of November 1956, had been renamed Political Investigation Department. More than ninety percent of its members were former ÁVH men, so that he could safely entrust them with carrying out merciless and bloody reprisals. Until the collapse of the communist regime in 1990, numerous members of the ÁVH operated in the ranks of state security.

KOMMUNISTA PROPAGANDAFILM
A NAGY IMRE ÉS KÖRE ELLEN
1958. JÚNIUSÁBAN ZAJLÓ „PERRŐL"

"Let's learn a little class-war from fascism's judiciary!"

(József Domokos, Supreme Court Judge, 28.03.1957)

TRAVESTY OF JUSTICE

Over 800 dossiers originating from the former Bureau of History are displayed in the room. Some of them contain copies of material relating to political trials, indictments, sentences, appeals, records of investigations from the period 1945-1956. The walls are lined with similar material, as are the benches and the judge's chair. The niche with its velvet-covered chair and telephone symbolizes the practice of arbitrary jurisprudence, insulting the principle of separation of powers and contrary to a constitutional state's prerequisite of judicial independence. The monitor shows a close on one-hour long propaganda film made in 1958 about the Imre Nagy trial.

After the end of the war and in accordance with the victorious Allies' directives, People's Courts were set up in Hungary. Their task was to call to account perpetrators of war crimes and crimes against the state and the people. The criminal proceedings, however, offered the chance to the nascent communist forces to abuse the powers of the People's Courts in order to eliminate their potential social and political opponents who stood in their way.

This entailed the abolition of judicial independence. More than a thousand judges were summarily dismissed, and hastily trained party faithfuls put in their places. Show trials were organized by the dozen (trial of the Hungarian Fellowship, the MAORT and Nitrokémia trials, etc.).

Equality before the law was done away with, and replaced by class-justice. This meant that an accused person's social origin – or as they called it, "class affiliation" – was taken into consideration either as a mitigating or an aggravating circumstance. The same act was punished far more harshly in the case of a kulak, a bourgeois or an aristocrat, than in the case of a poor peasant or a labourer. The destruction of the Hungarian propertied peasantry played a significant role in this type of sentencing. The so-called "kulak trials" affected some three hundred thousand individuals. They were deprived of their possessions, their freedom, in some cases of their lives, and invariably of their honour.

Hungarian justice – on the Soviet model – jettisoned the presumption of innocence, with the result that uncorroborated allegations could be used against an accused. Instead of evidence, confessions gained by torture were often regarded as sufficient. It was not the prosecutor who had to prove the guilt of the accused; the accused had to prove his innocence. The law no longer protected the citizen – it turned against him.

As of 1950 the autonomy of the courts ended formally as well. The Supreme Court came under the jurisdiction of the Minister of Justice (1950 art. IV).

In many cases severe punishments were meted out not on the basis of laws, but government decrees, such as sentences of 10 years' of imprisonment (2560/1949). Soldiers, who tried to escape to the West, were sentenced to death on the basis of secret, unpromulgated decrees. Their families were imprisoned on the pretext of having disobeyed the law of denunciation (1950 art. XXVI).

In those years more than 35,000 people were confined to jails, and at least as many again were awaiting prison sentences. In 1953, Imre Nagy opened the gates of the internment camps, and some 15,000 people received an amnesty, but rehabili-

tation and compensation were granted only to 474 ex-convicts who had belonged to the labour movement, nor did the number of court cases diminish. Between 1945 and 1956 close to 400 persons were executed for political reasons, and public proceedings were instituted against almost one in three adults. Retaliation by the Kádár regime against participants in the revolution and freedom fight of 1956 was conducted with unprecedented brutality. He introduced martial law, and one hundred and fifty-two capital sentences were carried out within one year. The age for the imposition of the death penalty was lowered to 16. Judge Tibor Vágó sentenced the underage Péter Mansfeld to death on the basis of this law. He was executed. The prohibition against the increase of punishment was not valid before the people's courts. Twenty-one death penalties were passed in the second instance, where the accused had received more lenient sentences in the first instance and had appealed for leniency or acquittal and the prosecution had not appealed against the original sentence. Before passing sentence, the judge discussed the matter with a so-called co-ordinating committee, comprising the local Party Secretary, Police Commissioner, the President of the Court and the Chief Public Prosecutor.
More than fifteen thousand persons were sentenced to prison terms for their part in attaining twelve days of freedom in 1956, and over the years more than two hundred were executed. Two hundred thousand fled the country.

"I don't think that Coca Cola would have stultifying effects."

(Népsport, 1952)

HALL OF PROPAGANDA AND DAILY LIFE

The first room acquaints us with the period's absurd and ridiculous propaganda resources and documents. In the next one contemporary posters and objects conjure up the communist workaday. The mind-set suggested by the crudely garish posters was just as mendacious and miserable as the ideology behind it.

BUDAPESTI NEMZETKÖZI
ŐSZI VÁSÁR 1949
ÉLJEN
A MUNKÁSOSZTÁLY
HARCI EGYSÉGE!
BÉKEKÖLCSÖNT
HYPO
KOLORÁDÓBOGÁR
JUT MINDENRE!
VERSENYFELHÍVÁS
SZABAD IFJÚSÁG
KONYVNA

CSEP
RUHABEMUTATÓ
CSEMEGE
MAGYAR RENDŐR
AGYŐZTES ORSZÁG
GY NAPJA
Gyertek dolgozni a bánya
MAGYARUL
PORSZÍVÓ
ÖTEVES TER
A BÉKE
Falusi dolgozó
ADOTT GABONA
OSAN VISSZATÉRÜL
MINDENT EGY HELYEN!
AZ ÁLLAMI ÁRUHÁZBÓL
NÉZZE MEG AZ EMBER
ÚJ!
ALUMINIUMBŐRÖND!
ORION
MAGYAR ALUMINIUMGYÁRTÁS REMEKE!
DIVATCSARNOK
YARTJA NÁDAS BŐRÖNDGYÁR . BUDAPEST
SZAB
RADIO

"Industry is ideology, the factories its producers. Although this caused shortages, there was a substantial production of words and working songs."

(Todorov)

THE ALUMINIUM ROOM

The display articles were manufactured of "Hungarian silver", i.e. bauxite, the raw material of aluminium, which can be seen in the centre of the hall. The drab, shoddy utensils exhibited on the surrounding shelves are characteristic elements of the period's daily life, the determinants of the general mood.

A
MAGYAR
EZÜST

"Every churchman, every gendarme, industrialist and landholder adores money, power, wealth, murders the people, hates the fatherland, is terrified of peace."

(Szabad Nép, 1951)

RELIGION

Monitors placed on the doors show documentaries about persecuted and imprisoned members of the clergy. Relics pertaining to the fate of the various persecuted are on display in the booths. The large, grey loudspeakers in the background recall the period's blaring propaganda; they emitted the veritably "ungodly" regime's "crusade" in public places.

Both Nazism – promoting racial war – and Communism – advocating class-war – regarded religion as their enemy. Whilst the totalitarian dictatorships persecuted and murdered their victims based on collective criteria, religion looks upon sin and practices forgiveness on the basis of individual responsibility. Both the Nazis and the communists replaced God with their own leaders, whom they presented as infallible and omniscient.

They swore allegiance to the leader, went into battle in his name, and surrounded his person with rituals befitting an idol. They proclaimed that they required men of a "new type" in order to create a "new world", a special "heaven on earth". They persecuted religion, the faithful and the churches, because ethico-religious teaching was diametrically opposed to the Nazi's and communists' ideologies, which they wanted to elevate to the rank of creeds.

Although in 1938-39 the leaders of the Christian churches in Hungary did not gainsay the shameful Jewish Laws, following the Nazi occupation, when their Jewish compatriots were in peril of their lives, a number of them hastened to their aid. The walls of churches, individual parishes, convents harboured many of the persecuted. Priests, pastors, nuns and many ordinary religious believers saved lives. The heroic courage of the Catholic Áron Márton, Vilmos Apor, Margit Slachta, the Calvinist József Élias, the Lutheran Gábor Sztehló are but a few shining examples.

From the very first, the communist dictatorship – launched in the wake of the Soviet occupying forces – regarded the Churches on account of their moral and spiritual authority, their financial power and international organization, as implacable enemies to be crushed. It was the aim of the communists to ruin the reputation of Church leaders and their institutions by demeaning them as reactionaries, as obstacles of progress. They trampled the moral authority of our priests and qualified it as a political crime if they stood up for their faith and for freedom of religion. They made every effort gradually to destroy the Churches and erode religious life. As a first step they expropriated the landholdings of the Catholic Church by way of the 1945 land reform. Although this measure threatened the majority of the Church's institutions with

financial ruin, in a letter issued on May 24, 1945 the episcopate expressed its hope that "the success of the new owners would compensate the Church for its losses and concerns."
The salaries granted to pastors, priests, rabbis were not in line with even the barest subsistence level. They banned all religious, devotional and charitable organizations. Apart from a few exceptions, all denominational schools were closed. In 1949 compulsory religious teaching was abolished and replaced by voluntarily organized "optional" religion classes. Children attending these, as well as their parents were constantly observed, harassed, ridiculed and threatened. Anyone graduating from a Church school was bound to be discriminated against in university entrance examinations.
Church leaders, who were reluctant to co-operate with the party-state, were eliminated by internal putsches, forced emigration, contrived court cases, prison sentences, threats.
The State Church Bureau (ÁEH), established in 1951, took charge of every denomination. With the help of the so-called "peace-priests", subservient to party politics (Miklós Beresztóczy, István Balogh, Richárd Horváth) and the bishops and church office-bearers (Ernő Mihályfi, János Péter, Iván Reök, József Darvas, László Dezséry, Lajos Vető) fraudulently elected from amongst party secretaries and communist functionaries, they tarnished the moral authority of the Churches. The new leaders stood for the interests of the party-state, agitated in favour of the peasantry's collectivization, took part in "peace work", and had their representatives in the Patriotic Peoples Front and in parliament.
The Churches' former leaders, pastors, priests were in jail or had been forced into total retirement. Scores of pastors, priests, monks and rabbis (e.g. Chief Rabbi Ferenc Hevesi) had to leave their homeland. By political and administrative means and intimidation they managed to force the signing of documents, which they called an "agreement", between the government and the Calvinist and Unitarian Churches respectively (October 7, 1948). They signed a similar agreement with the Lutheran and Jewish denominations two months later.
The prisons filled up with Catholic priests, monks and nuns. Even during the so-called soft dictatorship, i.e. in the sixties and seventies, they incarcerated young people accused of organizing Catholic or Calvinist-induced movements.
The two most respected Calvinist bishops, László Ravasz and Imre Révész raised their voices against the atrocities of the fledgling communist dictatorship as early as 1945. The new power treated the village pastors and priests as enemies from the first moment on. By July 1945 already thirty cases were registered of detained parish pastors in the diocese East of the Tisza. "Right-wing fascism has been replaced by left-wing fascism", declared Bishop Ravasz.
In 1948 the communist dictatorship set in motion the Churches' "systematization", the "separation of Church and State". In accordance with the rules of "newspeak", this expression meant its exact opposite. Never before had the Church been as closely intertwined with the oppressing statist power that threatened its very existence.
At the beginning of 1948 the party-state initiated a series of hitherto unheard of attacks. In March, the Calvinist General Superintendent Andor Lázár was first forced to resign by Ernő Mihályfi and subsequently detained at 60 Andrássy Road. A few weeks later, Bishop László Ravasz, president of the synod, was also forced to step down. In September 1949 it was the turn of Bishop Imre Révész. His successor was that János Péter, who, having abandoned his bishopric, later became the Foreign Minister in János Kádár's communist government. By 1950 the "changing of the guard" in the Calvinist Reformed Church became an accomplished fact.
One of the first actions of the Nyíregyháza police was the arrest and indictment of Zoltán Túróczi, Lutheran bishop of the Tisza diocese. He was sentenced to ten years penal servitude and loss of office on the charge of having committed war crimes. As a result of the various Church leaders' combined efforts he was discharged, but could not take up his bishopric until two years later. In August 1948 the ÁVO arrested Bishop Lajos Ordass, Superintendent of Schools Albert Radvánszky, and Sándor Vargha on the pretext of "irregularities related to the handling of foreign aid". Bishop Ordass was sentenced to two years penal servitude. Béla Kapi, Bishop of Transdanubia, together with three of his diocesan co-workers, resigned "of his own accord". The communists managed to have their own men elected to bishoprics: Lajos Vető in Nyíregyháza, and Lajos Dezséry in Budapest. Both of them resigned in 1956, but withdrew their resignations after the invasion of the Soviet military.

In 1955 a group of young Calvinist clergymen issued a declaration at the Reformed Theological Academy of Budapest. They were joined the following year by Bishop László Ravasz, who in his Memorandum summarized his views on the state of affairs in the Church. In the summer of 1956, they submitted a discussion paper signed by 160 clergymen to the Presidency of the Universal Conventicle, on the subject of the Church's renewal.
On October 31, the Movement for Renewal of the Reformed Church appealed to the compromised church leaders to resign, at the same time requesting László Ravasz to return to his former post. After the ruthlessly defeated Revolution, however, this could no longer take place. In 1957, the yet again firmly established dictatorship issued a directive, whereby church assemblies, and the publishing and copying of encyclicals where subject to the approval of the ÁEH. The collaborating leaders, who had resigned, were reinstated and brutal reprisals meted out to members of the renewal movement. In 1957 a number of priests, pastors and theologians were kept under observation and detained, while other Church dignitaries received high state decorations from the Kádár government. At the same time as the Calvinist bishop, Albert Bereczky expressed his gratitude to János Kádár in the name of all those who had been given medals, in Győr the sentence was carried out on the Calvinist clergyman Lajos Gulyás, who had been condemned to be hanged.
After the end of World War II, the Jewish denomination was faced with different problems to that of the Christian ones. After the persecution of the Jews, mass murders, deportations and the wave of emigration following the war, less than hundred and fifty thousand (1,4%) persons professed to be Jewish in the census of 1949. Hungarian Jewry, which had traditionally regarded itself as Hungarian by nationality and Jewish by religion, had suffered racial discrimination and horrendous persecution. As a consequence its dual affiliation loosened; because of that, and the promise of the establishment of a Jewish state, many of them became attracted to Zionism. (At the time of its abolition, the Hungarian Zionist Federation had 43 thousand members.) Zionism had a definite program and image for the future, and was not compatible therefore with the state-party's aims of total influence and supervision. Accordingly Jewish public life had to be "cleansed" of Zionists, bourgeois elements and all those who stood in the way of the party-state's unlimited dominance. The Communist Party's organization within the Jewish community was set up under the leadership of László Benedek, chief medical officer of the Jewish Hospital.
By 1950 Hungarian Jewry was gathered into a unified organization. Jews gradually became isolated from international Jewish organizations. All of a sudden Jewish associations became "imperialist spy networks", and their leaders arrested. Béla Berend, chief rabbi of Szigetvár was indicted for – of all things – having collaborated with the Arrow Cross. Several Zionist leaders were incarcerated in 1949; Géza Szűcs, the Hungarian head of the American Jewish Joint Distribution Company (an international charitable organ) and his twin brother József, the Jewish community's legal advisor, were forced into committing suicide, because they refused to hand over the list of those (Jews and non-Jews) receiving aid from them (August 11, 1951).
In 1953, on Soviet demand and according to the Soviet recipe, preparations were initiated for a great Zionist show trial. It has to be noted that in the Soviet-type regimes free play was given to overt anti-Semitism under the slogan of "anti-Zionism". For their own protection, party leaders frequently channelled the populace's mounting despair and grudge against the terror organs in the direction of anti-Semitism. This was so, because a significant number of party leaders and members of its terrorist organizations (PRO, ÁVO, ÁVH, KATPOL, GRO) were of Jewish origin, who did not only disavowe their God, but their country and their roots as well when they became the inhumane communist ideology's toadies. Party leaders of Jewish origin were among the detainees and several field-grade officers of the ÁVH, even Gábor Péter, as were the most prominent members of the Jewish community (who were accused, amongst others, of having killed Raoul Wallenberg), doctors, architects and engineers of Jewish descent.
The great days of reckoning were brought to a halt after the death of Stalin (March 5, 1953), and most of the prisoners were set free. The stigmatization and persecution of Zionism and the Zionists – following the Soviet example – lasted, however, until the change of regime.

"I stand for God, the Church and the country!"

(Cardinal József Mindszenty, 1956)

JÓZSEF MINDSZENTY

The room is a memorial to Cardinal Mindszenty. The monitors show clips of the salient events in his life and the communist propaganda campaign directed against him.

According to the data of the 1949 census, 70%, i.e. six and a half million of Hungary's population was of the Roman Catholic faith. For that reason the Catholic Church possessed the greatest social and political influence, as well as the most significant economic clout. Its network of educational, social, cultural and devotional institutions covered the entire country. The Catholic Church played a major role in nurturing and maintaining national culture and its traditions.
On October 7, 1945, the Vatican put a charismatic man at the head of the Hungarian Catholic Church, who said no to both terrorist dictatorships. As bishop of Veszprém, he had been through the wringer of Arrow Cross prisons, and from December 1948 onwards those of the communists. With Cardinal Mindszenty in the lead, the Catholic Church mobilized hundreds of thousands of faithfuls in defence of its institutions. The Church was concerned primarily about its schools and aggrieved about the abolition of compulsory religious education. Leading communists kept fanning the flames of hatred against Cardinal Mindszenty and the entire Catholic Church.
The police kept on harassing Church institutions and schools. Several dozen high-school students (their number is subject to debate and is estimated at 30-60) were carried off from Gyöngyös, together with their Franciscan schoolmaster, Father Szaléz Kis. The charge: the assassination of several Soviet soldiers at and around Gyöngyös between November of 1945 and January 1946. The father, the seventeen year-old youths Otto Kizmann and László Bodnár, as well as the sixteen year-old Sándor Kiss were executed on December 10, 1946. Their associates were sentenced to long terms of imprisonment and forced labour. The case of Father Szaléz Kiss was directed at 60 Andrássy Road by Lieutenant-Colonel Gyula Décsi. In January 1946 Rákosi gave out the watchword; "By the end of the year clerical reaction has to be eliminated". The communists launched a countrywide campaign in support of nationalizing denominational schools. On the pretext of an accidentally fired shot in Pócspetri (June 3, 1948), they initiated a crusade against the Catholic clergy, the devout Hungarian peasantry and the entire village. János Kádár, Gábor Péter and Miklós Vásárhelyi from the Szabad Nép visited the scene of the incident. The ÁVO occupied the village, and practically every inhabitant was molested. The whole country resounded with the call: "the clerical reaction has murdered a policeman". On June 20, 1948 Church schools were nationalized (6505 schools – over 5000 of these elementary schools). Soon after, the Churches were excluded from the sphere of healthcare and social work. By the withdrawal of the now "redundant" monastic orders' licences and the brutal treatment meted out to monks and nuns, they intimidated those Church leaders, who happened to be still at large.
By then – December 26, 1948 – they had arrested and later sentenced Cardinal József Mindszenty, head of the Roman Catholic Church. His trial presided over by Vilmos Olti at the People's Tribunal, lasted from February 3-8, 1949. The prosecutor was Gyula Alapi. During the course of the trial, public sentiment was whipped up to an unprecedented level. They tried to convince the intimidated country of Mindszenty's "crimes", of the "black reaction's" destructive, anti-democratic ferocity. The conviction of the Primate – and the communists were fully aware of this – did by no means suffice for forcing the Roman Catholic Church into subservience. They introduced the concept of "clerical reaction". From the Pope to the most insignificant village parish priest, all clerics now became reactionaries. The prisons became replete with priests and the harassment of the faithful laity became a routine affair. The Church tried to resist as long as it could. Finally, in the summer

of 1950, it retreated. The episcopate had to face the fact that the communists' cruelty and brutality was boundless. It reeled from the blow of the abolition of the monastic orders; it was distressed about the fate of its persecuted brethren, the more than ten thousand proscribed monks and nuns and its responsibility for their future. It had to admit its impotence and vulnerability. The bishops also feared that the movement of the "peace-priests" forced on the Church might cause a schism. They became despondent, because the strong and venerable Polish episcopate was also forced into an agreement with the socialist Polish state.

In its "concordat" the Catholic episcopate undertook to support the political system and the government of the Hungarian People's Republic, while the government gave a promise to uphold religious freedom and the free functioning of the Church. The Catholic Church regained eight of its schools and permission for its teaching orders to run them.

Less than a year later, the signatory of the agreement, József Grősz, Archbishop of Kalocsa, came into the firing line. József Révai, chief ideologue of the Communist Party, had worked out the strategy of the upcoming show trial. It was staged in the summer of 1951. Archbishop Grősz was sentenced to 15 years, Ferenc Vezér, a Pauline monk, received the death sentence; Vendel Endrédy, Abbot of Zirc was condemned to 14 years in prison, their co-defendants receiving long prison sentences. The ÁVH forced the bishops of Vác, Székesfehérvár and Szeged-Csanád to appoint peace-priests to important positions. In July 1951, led by Gyula Czapik Archbishop of Eger, the episcopate took the oath of loyalty to the constitution of the Hungarian People's Republic. The communists had accomplished their aim. The terror meted out by the ÁVH had broken the episcopate's resistance and extended the party-state's sphere of influence over the Catholic Church.

In 1956, Primate Mindszenty, liberated by the Revolution, once again took up the Church's leadership. On the day of the armed attack by the Soviets, he took refuge in the American Embassy. He spent fifteen years in self-imposed confinement in its Szabadság Square building. In 1971, under pressure from the Holy See and the Hungarian government, Mindszenty consented to emigrate. He lived for another four years. His ashes were brought home in 1991 and laid to rest in the Basilica of Esztergom. His beatification is in progress.

Pope John Paul II's visit to Hungary in August 1991 signalled the end of forty years of religious persecution.

"When they led me to my first major interrogation from the cellar of 60 Andrássy Road, I prayed to the Lord to erase from my mind the names of my friends."

(Abbot Vendel Endrédy, who spent six years in solitary confinement)

RECONSTRUCTED SUBTERRANEAN PRISON

The cellar of No. 60 Andrássy Road became notorious during the months of the Arrow Cross regime. Arrow Cross thugs hauled the people, whom they had rounded up, to the cellar of their headquarters, where they were brutally beaten up. They kept their victims for shorter or longer periods in the former coal cellars, where many of them lost their lives.

The communist political police moved into the horrible headquarters of the Arrow Cross in January 1945. They changed the "House of Loyalty" as a warning to the "House of Horrors". They soon outgrew the building and its cellar. During the course of the following years they came to occupy the entire block, underneath which they constructed an interconnected subterranean labyrinth. Prisoners, who were dragged off to be interrogated, were blindfolded and isolated from each other. Many of them seem to recall that the cellar of the building extended to several levels. When rebuilding the house, we found no indications of this. It is possible, though, that there did exist at the time cells that were dug out on a lower level in various other parts of the block.

Interrogations took place in upstairs rooms. Armed ÁVO-men stood guard before each room. Interrogations – in line with Soviet practice – were usually held at night. Suspects were prevented from sleeping for several nights, and in many cases were held without food and water. They employed every possible method of physical and psychological pressure on their victims. Facing the wall with their noses rammed against it, or with arms stretched out horizontally, sometimes for 10-12 hours. Beatings with truncheons were everyday affairs, as well as "physical exercises"; some were tortured with electric current, burning cigarettes, pliers. Detainees were not permitted to change their underwear, nor to take a bath, their daily ablutions could last a mere thirty seconds; they were not allowed to use towels, soap, toilet paper, toothpaste, tooth brushes, handkerchiefs. Prisoners were kept in cells with a lightbulb shining day and night. They weren't given blankets, nor a change of clothing. Often they were not allowed to go to the toilet, nor were there any buckets in the cells. Prisoners had to lie on wet plank beds, or even on the bare floor. Sadistic warders beat the detainees at every opportunity with rifle butts and truncheons. They were fed once a day, their ration a cupful of bean soup with 150 grams of bread, altogether 490 calories a day.

The cellar of No. 60 Andrássy Road was modified several times. All tell-tale traces were painstakingly removed. In one section of the cellar we have recreated the conditions under which political prisoners were kept in Hungary during the period of 1945 to 1956.

"Don't only guard them, hate them!"

(ÁVO slogan of the fifties)

PUNISHMENT CELLS

In the reconstructed cellar we present not only traditional cells, but also punishment cells, the condemned cell and the place of execution.

Detention cell: Solitary punishment cell, 60x50 cm floor space. 180 cm high. Two lightbulbs at eye-level, which shone into the prisoner's eyes during the entire time of punishment.
Wet cell: The detainee was forced to sit in water.
Fox-hole: Dark, low-ceilinged concrete cell, in which the prisoner could not straighten up.
Treatment room: We have placed the types of instruments of torture here, which were used to break the body and spirit of the prisoners.
Guard room: The ventilation apparatus used in the subterranean prison at No. 5 Belgrade Quay, which we discovered in 2000, can be seen here. The prison was two storeys below street level. The ventilation apparatus ensured the flow of air through a conduit traversing the cells. Individual cells could be cut off from this airflow as a means of punishment.
Condemned cell: condemned prisoners were kept here, whose appeals for clemency had been rejected.
Place of execution: The gallows used first in the Vác penitentiary and then until 1985 in the Kozma street prison, is exhibited here. (There were no executions in 60 Andrássy Road, "only" fatal bashings and suicides.)

"The ÁVH has brought to justice a whole series of harmful parasites, who wanted to ruin the country."

(Szabad Nép, 1950)

INTERNMENT

The political police set up internment camps at Recsk, Kistarcsa, Tiszalök and Kazincbarcika, and dozens of closed camps operated in the eastern part of the country. A miners' car and rocks from Recsk are displayed in the hall, as well as keepsakes made in the camp (a cigarette lighter, glasses, a cross, a cigarette-box, "news" written onto cigarette paper). Film clips can be seen and heard, presenting the recollections of former internees.

After the country was occupied by Soviet forces, the new Hungarian government issued an unpublished decree, regulating the stipulations of internment. Internment, that is to say "placing someone under police surveillance", was the regime's technique for isolating and cutting off from public life its real and supposed enemies. Internment gave the authorities – above all the political police – unlimited power to eliminate from society – without any previous investigation on mere suspicion or on the basis of political considerations – citizens who stood in the regime's way. Internment was resorted to in cases where there was not enough evidence for arresting a person.

Not only the members of extreme right-wing organizations, former army officers, gendarmes, spreaders of Arrow Cross and Nazi propaganda, or the country's former political leaders, public servants were interned, but anyone whom the communists regarded as their enemies. Internment was a tool by which the communists, aiming for unlimited power, could settle scores with their political opponents.

Between 1945 and 1948, in the course of barely three years, the ÁVO interned more than forty thousand people all over the country. Until the spring of 1950, the political police ran four central, concentration camp-like internment camps at Recsk, Kistarcsa, Tiszalök and Kazincbarcika, where many thousands of prisoners performed hard-labour. Apart from these, several dozen smaller camps functioned in various parts of the country. Learning from Nazi and Soviet methods, the victims were put to work in coal and metal mines, quarries, road construction and in the timber industry under inhuman conditions, with primitive tools. The maximum period of internment was at first 24 months, to be reviewed each month under the terms of legislation in force; however, most of the victims were confined for a far longer time without being able to communicate with their families. These detainees, isolated from everything and everybody, were at the mercy of the warders' baser instincts. "We don't have to account for the prisoners!" became their catchphrase.

In addition, there were some dozen so-called closed camps in the eastern part of the country. They were filled from 1948 onward with entire families, especially from the Eastern, Southern, Western regions.

Following the issue on July 26, 1953 of the decree abolishing the internment camps, these were gradually disbanded,

but because the review of numerous cases was purposely delayed, many prisoners were transferred to the ÁVH's prisons, and several hundred were released only in 1956. In the post-revolutionary period of retribution the communists once again resorted to the process of internment and reopened some of the former camps.
In the second half of 1961, the Kádár regime decided on the concentration of some 10,000 unreliable individuals, who posed a danger to society in "suitable camps" "in the event of an emergency". The implementation of the plan was worked out by the ÁVH's successor, the State Security Service. The emergency plan, with slight variations, remained in force until the collapse of the regime.
Youngsters of military age, who were considered by the regime to be "class-aliens", i.e. enemies, were also subjected to cruel harassment. Many a scion of aristocratic and even upper- and middle-class families, as well as peasant boys, whose parents were "kulaks", was drafted as a labour-serviceman within the framework of the Hungarian People's Army. Instead of military training, unreliable labour-servicemen had to undergo "special training". They were housed in camps fenced in by barbed-wire and put to work in mines and the construction of roads and military airfields. The aim, however, was not production, but the youngsters' physical and psychological humiliation. Their number in 1952 amounted to 10,899, and rose to 12,511 the following year. The institution of labour service was discontinued in 1956.

"What seemed impossible, has come to pass: the people themselves have defeated a totalitarian state."

(Raymond Aron)

1956

The hall conjures up the Revolution's events, and is a memorial to the fallen heroes. We can view here the leather coat of Gergely Pongrátz, the coat of one of the victims of the Mosonmagyaróvár fusillade, as well as a DP automatic rifle. A Molotov cocktail and a bicycle fork damaged by a shell can be seen in the glass case.

Stalin died on March 5, 1953. A power struggle ensued in the Kremlin. On June 17 a mass rising took place in Berlin against the communist regime and the Soviet occupation. Within two days, Soviet troops and the GDR's militia crushed the uprising with ruthless violence. In the spring of 1955 the victorious powers of World War II signed the Austrian State Treaty. Austria became an independent, neutral state and all occupying forces were pulled out from her territory. The Soviet special corps that had hitherto been stationed in Austria was withdrawn to Hungary. One day prior to the signing of the Austrian Treaty, Hungary, under the leadership of András Hegedűs, joined the Warsaw Pact, providing a legal basis for the Soviet army's continued presence in the country.

On February 25, 1956, in his address to the Twentieth Congress of the Communist Party of the USSR, Khrushchev, the Party's new First Secretary, unmasked the crimes of the Stalinist era. In the eyes of many, the communist system became morally tainted.

On October 23, 1956 demonstrations broke out in Budapest and several other cities. It was the student body which drew up the demands, and the young people who organized the protest marches in support of events in Poland. In no time they were joined by vast crowds. No wonder; after all, almost every stratum of the populace had been detrimentally affected by the dictatorship that impinged on the country's entire social and economic life.

When the secret police opened lethal fire on the unarmed demonstrators first in Debrecen and then at Broadcasting House in Budapest, what had so far been a massive movement of protest against the die-hard communist elite, turned into open revolution. Its objective: the radical transformation of society, the creation of an independent, free and democratic Hungary. Armed clashes commenced at Broadcasting House, whence they spread, becoming a freedom fight after the intervention of Soviet forces. In Budapest, the spontaneously formed groups of insurgent freedom fighters became increasingly better organized, and especially more successful in their battles against Soviet and Hungarian soldiers.

The civil population showed its hostility to the communist dictatorship almost everywhere, by disabling or disbanding state and local institutions. On October 28 the Soviet and Hungarian political and military leadership was forced to give ground. Prime Minister Imre Nagy, swept into power by the Revolution, ordered a general and immediate truce, and the following day the Soviet troops began their withdrawal from the capital. Negotiations were initiated for their withdrawal from the

country itself. The government abolished the hated and dreaded State Security Department and on October 30, Nagy went on the air to announce that the one-party system was being abolished. He also pledged free elections.
Despite considerable ideological differences of opinion, the democratic institutions brought into being during the Revolution – National Committees, Workers' Councils, Revolutionary Military Councils, Militia Corps and democratic political parties – subscribed to the same goal: the creation of a democratic and independent Hungary.
On October 30, the government of the USSR announced that it wished to amend its relationship with the "fraternal socialist countries", and a bare 24 hours later gave out the order to crush the Hungarian freedom fight. Additional Soviet troops crossed the Hungarian border. In reply, the Hungarian government withdrew from the Warsaw Pact, proclaimed Hungary's neutrality, and asked the United Nation's assistance. However, it was unable to stop Soviet aggression.
On November 4, Soviet tanks brutally bore down on the revolutionaries, and by the middle of the month managed to break the more-or-less organized armed resistance, which was futilely attempting to protect the Revolution's achievements.
The Moscow-designated puppet government, the Revolutionary Worker-Peasant Party, led by János Kádár, deployed every dictatorial and terrorist means against masses protesting against the Soviet military occupation.
Budapest was once again in ruins. The number of wounded was about 20,000, more than two and a half thousand died – two thousand of these in the capital. Approximately two hundred thousand left the country. The Soviets arrested some five thousand persons, 860 of them – a number of under-age boys and girls – were carried off by the KGB to the Soviet Union as prisoners of war. Three hundred to four hundred and fifty fell as a result of the murderous fusillades. Close on fifteen thousand people were arrested on the order and with the help of the Soviet advisors, and two hundred and twenty nine were executed. In June of 1958, Prime Minister Imre Nagy and three other major figures of the Revolution were sentenced to death in camera, and executed.

"The Hungarian people now hang on the trees."

(Sándor Márai)

REPRISALS

Records of executions and rejected appeals for clemency are shown on replica scaffolds. The names of the martyrs can be heard from the loudspeakers.

"You were Hungarian, that's why."

(Sándor Márai)

EMIGRATION

Two hundred thousand people left Hungary after the Revolution of 1956. The film clip on the monitor conjures up their flight. Postcards written to their loved ones cover the walls of this hall.

"And in place of tears, the wrinkles, trickle down, the empty trench trickles

(János Pilinszky)

HALL OF TEARS

On the walls: names of those who were executed for political reasons between 1945 and 1967.

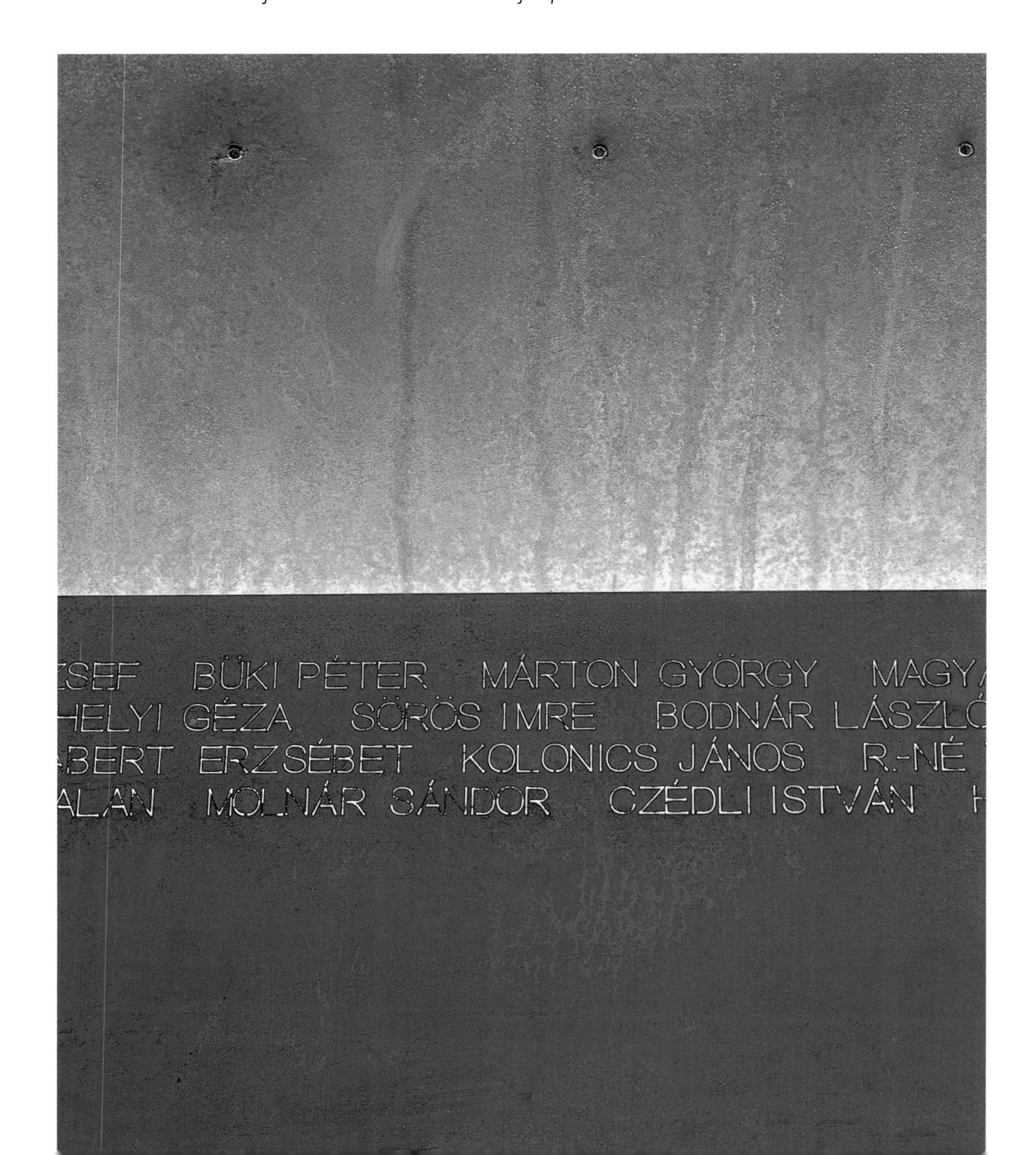

'We now lock fear and hatred behind bars, because we do not want them to have a place in our future lives. We shall lock them behind bars, but shall not forget them."

(Prime Minister Viktor Orbán at the opening of the House of Terror, 2002)

FAREWELL

Monitors in the last hall show the mass demonstrations of the late 1980s, protests against the Bős-Nagymaros dam and the demolishing of Hungarian villages in Romania, as well as the reburial of Imre Nagy and his confederates; the visit of John Paul II to Hungary and the last Soviet troops leaving the country. The sequence concludes with shots of the museum's opening on February 24, 2002.

"...he willingly killed for pleasure not only on command."

(Miklós Radnóti: Fragment, May 19, 1944)

THE PERPETRATORS' WALL

The hallway is lined with pictures of the two repressive regimes' yes-men and stooges: Arrow Cross and communist leaders, ÁVO-men and Arrow Cross shock-troopers. Perpetrators are all those, who took an active part in establishing and maintaining the two Hungarian totalitarian terror regimes (Arrow Cross and communist), as well as those, who held responsible positions in the executive organs of these two regimes. The majority of these people served or held responsible positions in organizations where crimes against humanity and war crimes were committed, acts which were incompatible even with their own legal systems. The perpetrators either took part in such crimes, or gave orders for their implementation, or sanctioned such decisions, or supported them as instigators. Their behaviour during their earlier or subsequent careers does not absolve them from personal responsibility.

With especial regard to the members and officeholders of the following organizations:

Hungarian Arrow Cross Party – Hungarist Movement: members of the district staff and higher ranking office-holders.
Hungarian Arrow Cross Party – Hungarist Movement: armed shock-troopers
Members of the National Retribution Organ (A sort of Arrow Cross political police) Members of the Szálasi government
The National Leader's Working Staff
The permanent staff of the Political Police Department
The permanent staff of the ÁVO
The permanent staff of the ÁVH
Members of the MKP, MDP and MSZMP (1945-1961)
Ministers of Justice (1945-1961)
Head of the MDP's Administrative Department (1950-1961)
Presidents of the Supreme Court (1945-1961)
Chief Prosecutors (1945-1961)

TETTESEK
VICTIMIZERS

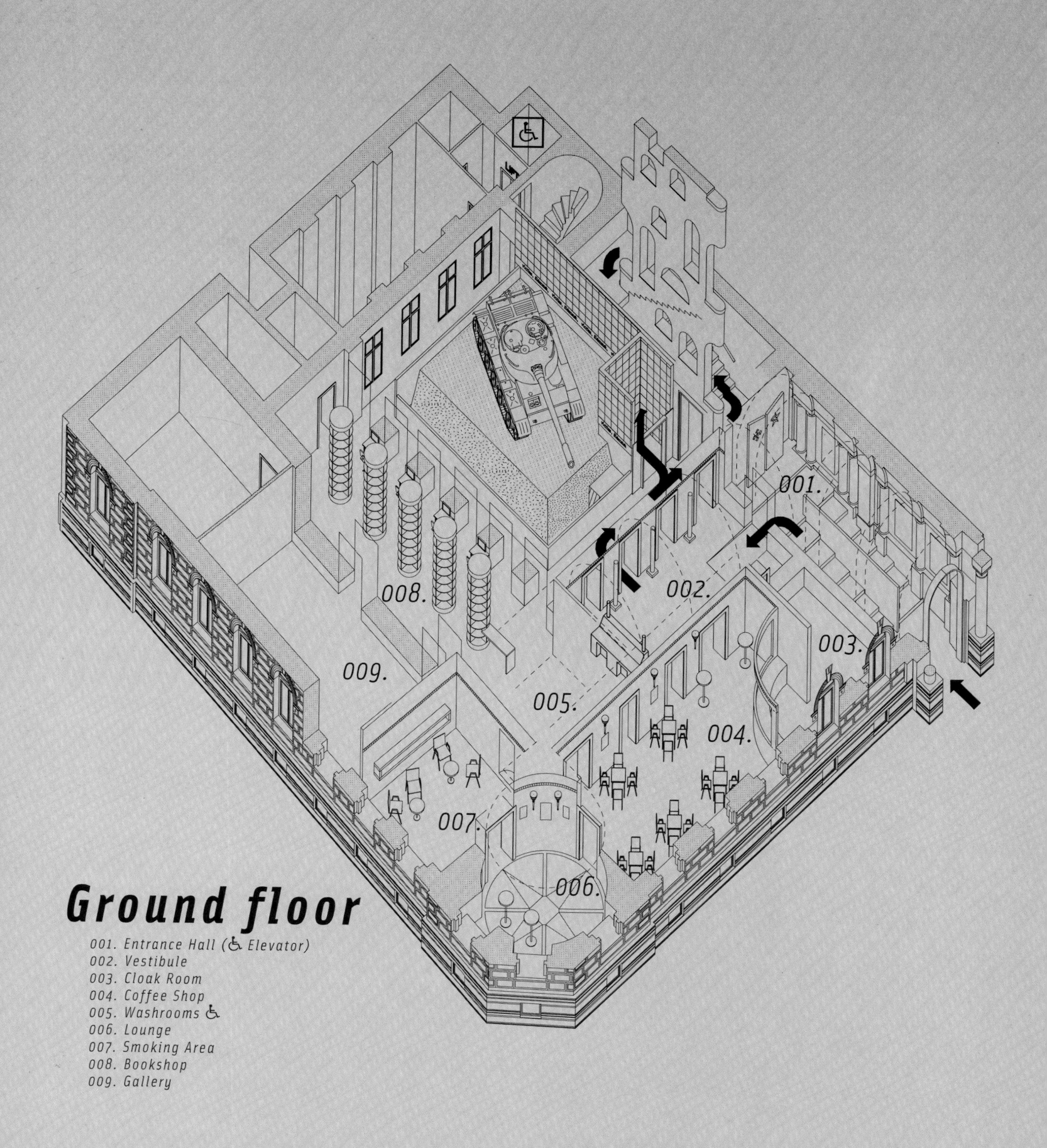

Ground floor

001. Entrance Hall (♿ Elevator)
002. Vestibule
003. Cloak Room
004. Coffee Shop
005. Washrooms ♿
006. Lounge
007. Smoking Area
008. Bookshop
009. Gallery

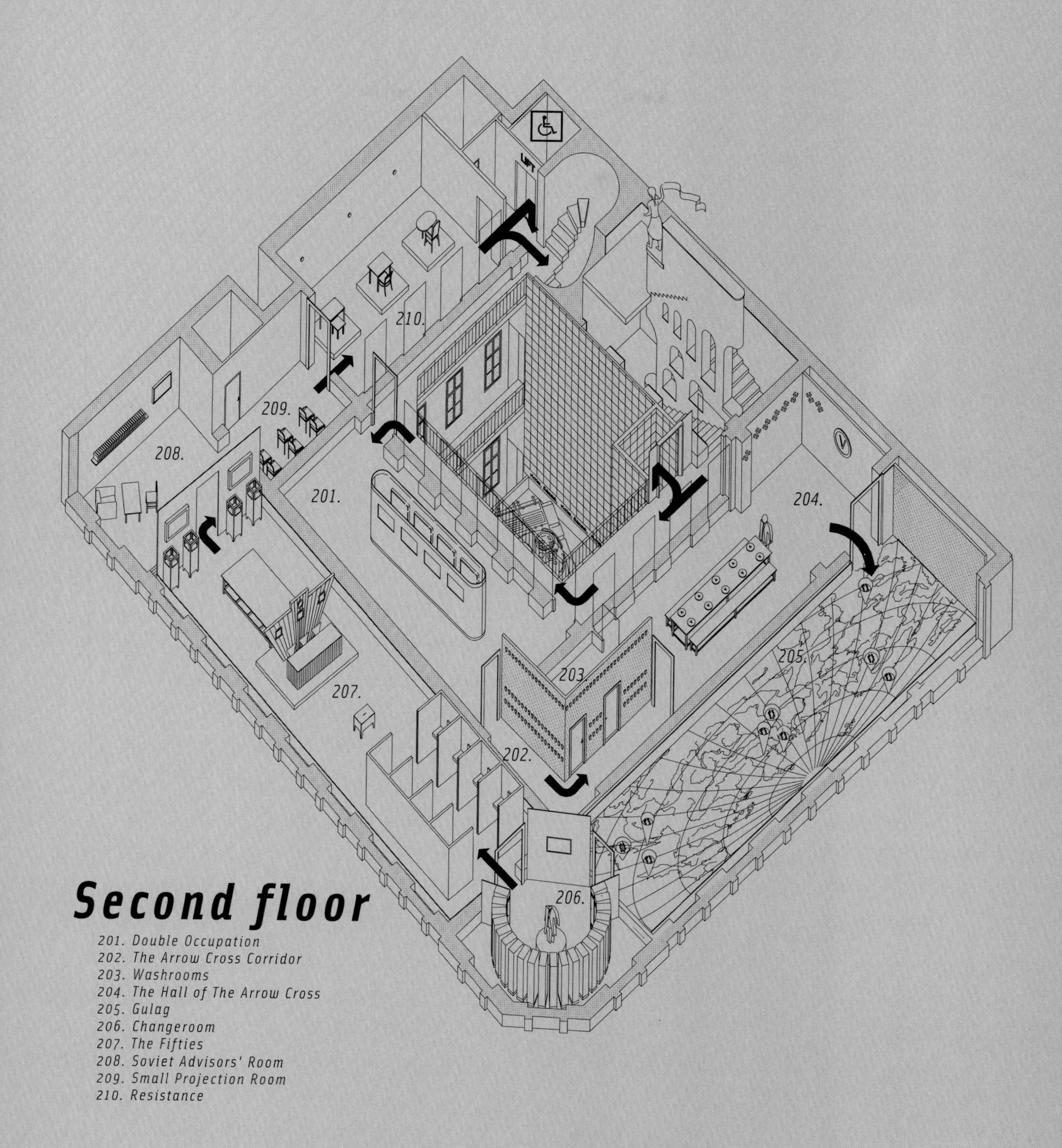

Second floor

201. Double Occupation
202. The Arrow Cross Corridor
203. Washrooms
204. The Hall of The Arrow Cross
205. Gulag
206. Changeroom
207. The Fifties
208. Soviet Advisors' Room
209. Small Projection Room
210. Resistance

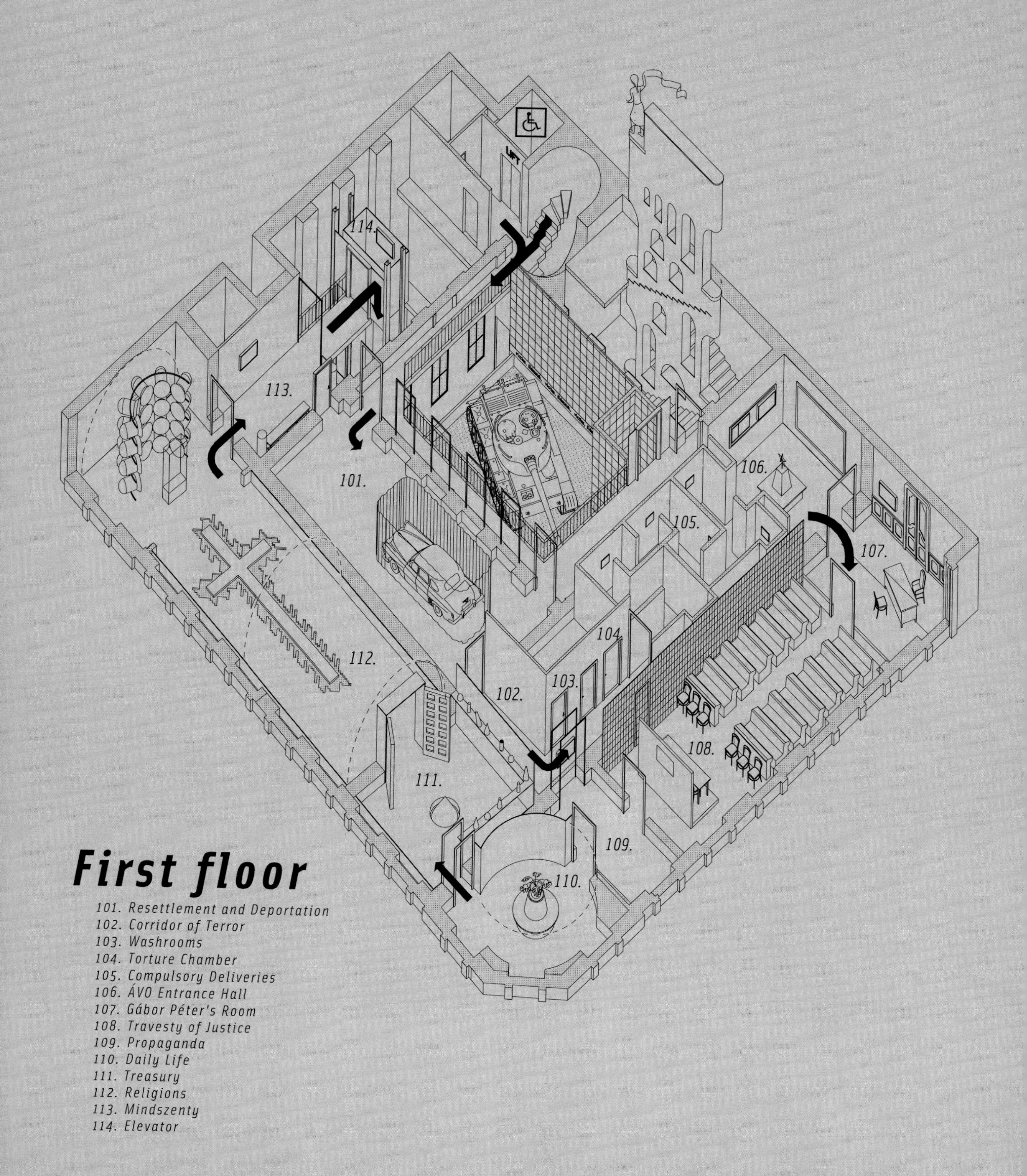
LIFT
113.
114.
101.
106.
105.
107.
104.
112.
103.
102.
108.
111.
109.
110.
First floor
101. Resettlement and Deportation
102. Corridor of Terror
103. Washrooms
104. Torture Chamber
105. Compulsory Deliveries
106. ÁVO Entrance Hall
107. Gábor Péter's Room
108. Travesty of Justice
109. Propaganda
110. Daily Life
111. Treasury
112. Religions
113. Mindszenty
114. Elevator

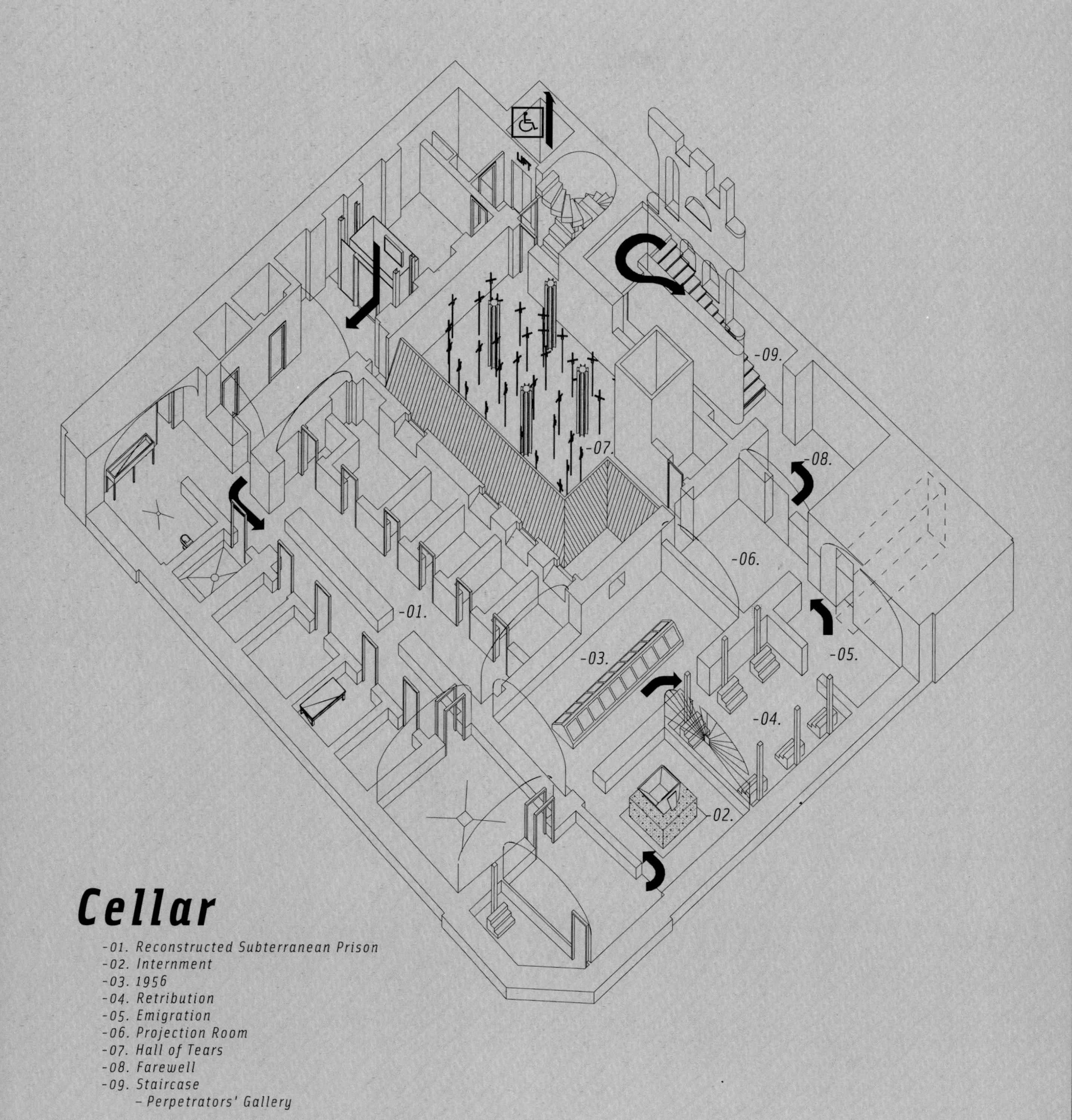
-01.
-02.
-03.
-04.
-05.
-06.
-07.
-08.
-09.
Cellar
-01. Reconstructed Subterranean Prison
-02. Internment
-03. 1956
-04. Retribution
-05. Emigration
-06. Projection Room
-07. Hall of Tears
-08. Farewell
-09. Staircase
– Perpetrators' Gallery

Victims

We have placed photos of the two totalitarian regimes' victims on the walls of the punishment cells. Of those, who sacrificed their lives or freedom in the fight against oppression, and those who were carried off to the gulag.

VICTIMS OF THE REVOLUTION OF 1956 AND THE FREEDOM FIGHT

Angyal, István (1928–1958) - Construction works manager. Deported to Auschwitz in 1944 with his mother and one of his sisters; he alone returned. Because of his open espousal of Georg Lukács, expelled after two years of study from the Arts Faculty of the ELTE (Eötvös Loránd University). Took part in the revolutionary movement from October 23 to 27, 1956, before long becoming leader of the Tűzoltó Street group. Between November 4 and 8 joined the fight with his group against attacking Soviet troops; until his arrest on November 16 wrote and distributed leaflets. Condemned to death on several charges, such as inciting rebellion. Executed on December 1, 1958.

Bárány, János (1930–1959) - Ironworker. Joined the demonstrators on October 23, 1956, and subsequently took part in the fighting. Elected as leader by the Tompa Street revolutionary group on October 25 or 26. Took up the fight with his group against the Soviet troops several times even after November 4. Collected weapons and ammunition, printed and distributed leaflets. Continued his resistance activities after the defeat of the Revolution. Elected to the Csepel workers council, eventually becoming President of the Revolutionary Youth Association (Young Workers). Arrested on April 20, 1957, sentenced to death and executed.

Brusznyai, Árpád (1924–1958) - Ancient historian, philologist, teacher. Elected to the Veszprém County Revolutionary Council on October 26, 1956; became its leader on November 1. The Revolutionary Council called for the government to initiate negotiations for the Soviet troops to leave Hungary and to announce democratic elections. Arrested on April 25, 1957 and sentenced in the first instance to life imprisonment. On January 7, 1958 sentence changed to death on request of the County Party Secretary. Sentence carried out two days later.

Dudás, József (1912–1957) - Took part for many years in the Romanian (Transylvanian) illegal communist movement, and was jailed on several occasions. Present in Moscow at the armistice negotiations. Imprisoned on trumped up charges in Hungary (Recsk) and Romania from 1946 to 1954 and later worked as a mechanical engineer. Joined in the revolutionary actions at Széna Square, and organized the second district National Committee. In his program, issued on behalf of the All-Hungarian National Revolutionary Committee, demanded the creation of a multi-party system, a coalition government and the announcement of neutrality. Arrested by the Soviets on November 21. Court-martialled, charged with organizing and leading an uprising, sentenced to death and executed on January 19, 1957.

Gimes, Miklós (1917–1958) - Journalist, politician. Called up for labour service during World War II. Joined the Communist Party in 1945. Wrote for the Szabad Nép and later the Magyar Nemzet. In May, 1955 expelled from the Party and fired from his job for demanding reassessment of unlawful trials. Reinstated to the Szabad Nép editorial staff on October 22, 1956. During the Revolution founded his own paper, the Magyar Szabadság, in which he supported the Revolution's aims. After November 4, edited an illegal paper, the "Október Huszonharmadika" ("Twenty-third of October"). Arrested by the Soviets on December 5. After conclusion of legal proceedings against him personally, sentenced to death and executed as the third party in the trial of "Imre Nagy and Accomplices".

Iván Kovács, László (1930–1957) – Football player. On October 23, 1956, getting his hands on some weapons joined the fight against the Soviet troops in Budapest. On October 25, joined the armed group at Corvin Lane, becoming their leader the following day. From the beginning of November, second-in-command to the new leader. On November 4 fought Soviet troops, but the same day some of his colleagues declared him a traitor and arrested him. Escaping and keeping his weapon, went into hiding, and in February 1957 organized an illegal party and distributed leaflets. Arrested on March 12, 1957, sentenced to death and executed at the end of December.

Krassó, György (1932–1991) – Participant in the 1956 Revolution, opposition politician. Studied economics from 1951 until expelled in 1955. Expelled from the Party for "destructive conduct" in 1952 and deprived of his scholarship. Fought in 1956, and mimeographed "seditious" leaflets after the second Soviet intervention. Arrested on November 15, 1956. Released by amnesty in the spring of 1963. Took part in opposition movements from 1979. Collaborated with the artists' group "Inconnu". In 1982 established his own samizdat publishing house, Magyar Október. Migrated to England in 1985; worked for Radio Free Europe and the BBC. Returned home on June 15, 1989.

Losonczy, Géza (1917–1957) – Came in contact with the communist movement during his scholarship years in Paris. On his return wrote for the Népszava, and after 1942 went undercover. Held high Party and state positions after the war until 1951. Arrested on trumped up charges and sentenced to 15 years imprisonment. Released in 1954. Became member of the intra-Party opposition group headed by Imre Nagy. After October 23, 1956 member of Party leadership, and from October 30 member of Imre Nagy's government. Fled to the Yugoslav embassy on November 4. Arrested together with members of the Imre Nagy group. Lost his life on December 21, 1957 while on remand under hitherto unexplained circumstances.

Maléter, Pál (1917–1958) – Army officer. After graduating from the Ludovika Military Academy fought at the Eastern front, where he was wounded and taken prisoner. Volunteered to fight against the Nazis. He was deployed in Transylvania in command of a detachment. In 1945 was made commander of the battalion, organized to guard the Provisional Government. On October 24, 1956 went to the Kilian Barracks, where he joined the Revolution on October 28. Became first deputy of the Minister of Defence, was soon after named Minister of Defence and promoted to brigadier-general. Arrested by Soviet State Security in Tököl on November 3, while military leader of deputation negotiating the withdrawal of Soviet troops. Sentenced to death in the trial of "Imre Nagy and Accomplices", and executed.

Mansfeld, Péter (1941–1959) – Trade school student. Joined the Széna Square revolutionaries in October, 1956. Carried weapons and ammunition by car to the insurgents. On November 5 forcibly entered the residence of former Minister of the Interior, László Piros and later concealed the weapons he had looted there. In 1958 decided with his friend to start a resistance group with weapons seized from the police and militia. On February 17, 1958, they therefore abducted the policeman guarding the Austrian embassy, whom they disarmed and let go. Two days later Mansfeld was arrested. Sentenced to life imprisonment, later sentenced to death. Executed eleven days prior to his 18th birthday.

Nagy, Imre (1896–1958) – Communist politician, agronomist. After 1945 minister of agriculture, then minister of the interior, later minister for collecting surplus produce and livestock. Expelled from the Party leadership for unorthodox views, he was, however, made prime minister in 1953 on Soviet initiative. Relieved from his post and expelled from the Party in 1955. On October 23, 1956 was reinstated into the Party leadership and appointed prime minister in responses to the demonstrators' demands. Fled to the Yugoslav embassy on November 4, was arrested by the Soviets on December 22 and deported with his family and associates to Romania. Sentenced to death on June 15, 1958 and executed the following day.

Szabó, János (1897–1957) – Labourer, driver. Member of Communist Party from 1945 to 1949. Fled to Yugoslavia, was apprehended there, interned and "thrown back" to Hungary, where he was sentenced to 3 months jail. Re-arrested in 1953 indicted for espionage. After the outbreak of the Revolution, joined the Széna Square insurgents on October 25, whose leader he became forthwith. At the end of October he relocated the group to the former Maros Street State Security barracks. They resisted the Soviet troops for several days, then gradually evacuating Széna Square, withdrew in small units in the direction of the Buda hills. Arrested on November 19, was sentenced to death and executed.

Szilágyi, József (1917–1958) – Lawyer, politician. Chief Superintendent of the Debrecen Police at the end of 1944, subsequently participated in organizing the national police administration on the Communist Party's behest. Was removed in 1949 as head of the Party's Military and Police Department. At the beginning of 1956 was expelled from the Party as well. On October 22 took part and addressed the general meeting at the University of Technology. As member of a delegation visited Imre Nagy on October 27 to convince him of the necessity for changing the political course. From October 28, leader of Imre Nagy's secretariat. Fled with his family to the Yugoslav embassy on November 4. He too was deported to Romania after December 22. His case was separated from the trial of "Imre Nagy and Accomplices"; received the death sentence and was executed.

Tóth, Ilona (1932–1957) – Medical student. In October, 1956 attached to the Szövetség Street hospital for training in internal medicine. When reporting for duty on October 25, was redirected to the Péterfy Sándor Street hospital. Joined the Voluntary Ambulance Service, and from November 1 until her arrest was in charge of the Péterfy hospital's auxiliary section.

After the end of fighting, took part in the political resistance: preparing leaflets and was involved in editing the illegal newspaper Élünk ("We're alive"). Arrested on November 20, 1956. Accused of murder, she was sentenced to death and executed.

VICTIMS OF THE COMMUNIST DICTATORSHIP

Almásy, Pál (1902–1985) – Professional officer, lieutenant general. Joined the military resistance movement in the autumn of 1944. Was arrested by the National Retribution Organ. Condemned to death, but sentence changed to 15 years imprisonment. After 1945 became the Independent Smallholder Party's military expert and nominee for Minister of Defence. Arrested in 1950 and sentenced to death in the trial of László Sólyom. His sentence was commuted to penal servitude for life. Released in 1955. Rehabilitated in 1991.

Bilkey-Papp, Zoltán (1924–1951) – Medical student, dissenter. Member of an armed anti-Soviet resistance group, the Magyar Front. Arrested in 1946 and sentenced to death for distributing leaflets, anti-democratic plotting and war crimes. The latter charge was due to his having served during the siege of Budapest with the Vannay-brigade on the Nazi's side.

Although given a reprieve by the president of the republic, was executed on January 24, 1951 on the order of Sándor Rónai, president of the presidential council.

Dénes, Béla (1904–1959) – Medical doctor, Zionist leader. Member of the Hungarian Social Democratic Party, co-President of the Hungarian Zionist Association, member of the editorial board of the Hungarian Jewish weekly, Új Élet. Assisted young Hungarian Zionists illegally to cross the border. Was arrested in May, 1949 by the anti-Zionist communist authorities. Sentenced to three years penal servitude as the principal defendant in the Zionist trial. Worked as a doctor in prison and the Kistarcsa internment camp. Released in 1954, he emigrated to Israel in 1957.

Domonkos, Miksa (1890–1954) – Captain of the reserve, mechanical engineer. After Hungary's occupation by the Nazis, helped to save many lives. From April 1944 member of the Jewish Council. From 1948 acting secretary of the Jewish Community of Pest.
Arrested by the ÁVH in 1953 in preparation for the Zionist trial. After merciless tortures released on November 13 in a critical condition. Never recovered. Passed away in February, 1954.

Donáth, György (1904–1947) – Politician, as of 1939 parliamentary deputy of the Magyar Élet Pártja (MÉP = Hungarian Life Party), from 1943 its national vice-president. In 1939 joined the Hungarian Fraternal Community. Arrested by the ÁVO in December 1946 as one of the Hungarian Fraternal Community's leaders. Was sentenced to death on April 16, 1947 in the first big political trial aimed at destroying the Independent Smallholders Party, the so-called "anti-republic plot", and executed on October 23, 1947. Rehabilitated in 1991.

Geiger, Imre (1900–1950) – Engineer. Managing director of the Budapest Standard Co., an electrical and communications firm with American financial interests. As it was important for the communists to acquire the company, he was accused of "American imperialist sabotage against the people". Arrested by the Security Service; charged with espionage and supplying information to foreign powers, was sentenced to death and executed in 1950.

Hadváry, Pál (1908–1948) – Professional soldier, colonel. One of the most highly-decorated officers of World War II. Arrested in 1946 by the Defence Ministry's Military Political Department and extradited to the Soviet military authorities. After his release reinstated into the Hungarian army. From 1947 head of the Kossuth Academy's training and studies, later its second-in-command. In 1947 got in touch with émigré resistance groups, specifically with the Fellowship of Hungarian Brothers-at-Arms. Undertook organization of anti-communist resistance and intelligence gathering. Arrested in 1948 for treason by the Military Political Department. Sentenced to death and executed.

Kelemen, Gyula (1897–1973) – Toolmaker, social-democrat politician. In 1945 member of the Pest county and Újpest National Committee. Parliamentary deputy until 1948, later Under-Secretary in the Ministry of Trade. As an influential politician of the Social Democratic Party, opposed its merger with the communists, was therefore arrested in connection with the Nitrokémia-case and in 1948 sentenced to life imprisonment. Released by amnesty in 1956. In October, 1956 took part in re-organizing the Social Democratic Party, and on October 31 appointed its secretary-in-chief. From November 2 to 4 Minister of State in the Imre Nagy government. Rehabilitated in 1963.

Kéri, Kálmán (1901–1994) – Officer, colonel-general. Chief of Staff of the First Army prior to October 15, 1944. After the war instrumental in organizing the new Hungarian army. Interned by the communists 1949-1953 at Kistarcsa and Recsk. Sentenced to four years imprisonment on December 3, 1953 retrospectively to justify his detention. After the change of regime, was appointed brigadier-general in 1990 and colonel-general in 1992. From 1990 until his demise parliamentary deputy of the MDF.

Kéthly, Anna (1889–1976) – Social democrat politician, publicist. Between 1922 and 1944 parliamentary deputy. From 1945 to 1948 Vice-President of the House. Opposed merger of social democrats and communists, was therefore expelled from her party in 1948. Arrested in 1950, subsequently found guilty on trumped-up charges in 1954. Released that same year due to international pressure, but kept under police surveillance until the autumn of 1956. During the Revolution elected president of the newly-formed Social Democratic Party. On November 2 appointed Minister of State in the Imre Nagy government. Left country at news of Soviet attack, and represented Hungary's cause in the United Nations.

Révay, Kálmán (1911–1950) – Officer, brigadier-general. Pensioned off in 1944. Joined the military resistance movement. Arrested on November 22, 1944, sentenced to death on December 8, sentence commuted to 10 years imprisonment. Deported to Germany in spring of 1945. After his return to Hungary assisted in the new Hungarian army's organization. Was Commander of the Kossuth Academy. In 1950 arrested on trumped-up charges and executed in 1950. Rehabilitated in 1955.

Ungár, József (1932–1953) – Head of the Veszprém Sports Organization, dissident. One of his close acquaintances found the body of a man battered to death. When it came to light that he had been murdered by men of the Veszprém State Security Police, Ungár and his friends organized a resistance group, sending one of their own to the West to make contacts. Members of the group acquired weapons. József Ungár was arrested in 1952 on charges of espionage. Executed in 1953.

Zsedényi, Béla (1894–1955) – Jurist, journalist, politician. From December 1944 President of the Provisionary National Assembly, from May, 1945 also President of the National Supreme Council. Elected member of National Assembly as a highly regarded public figure. After election of new President of the Republic, made President of House of Representatives. His seat received as representative of the Independence Party was abolished on communist pressure in 1947. Arrested and convicted in 1950 on the bogus charge of plotting against the state. Died in prison.

BEARERS OF TESTIMONY TO THE FAITH

Apor, Vilmos (1892–1945) – Roman Catholic bishop. In the summer of 1944 wrote to the Primate, Jusztinian Serédi to persuade him to take a strong stance against the government. He even appealed to Gestapo headquarters in an attempt to free the Jews of Győr from the ghetto. Negotiated with the Nazi military command to spare the town from a siege. He was shot on Good Friday 1945 by a Red Army major, as he protected women who had taken refuge from the marauding Soviet soldiers in his residence. The women were saved, but the bishop died of his wounds on Easter Monday, 2 April 1945. Beatified in 1997.

Asztalos, János (1910–1995) – Roman Catholic priest. Parish priest of Pócspetri 1945-1948. In June 1948, during a mass-meeting protesting against the nationalization of the parish school, one of the two policemen sent to the scene was fatally wounded due to an accident. Exploiting the event, the Communist Party initiated a show trial with the aim of tarnishing the reputation of the "reactionary clergy". Accused of incitement to wilful homicide, János Asztalos was sentenced to death, which was commuted to life imprisonment. Released in 1956, he left for the West. Returned to Hungary in 1989.

Baranyay, Jusztin (1882–1956) – Member of the Cistercian order, Catholic priest. Internationally recognized expert on canon law. One of the leading personalities of the legitimist (royalist) movement in the inter-war years. Secondary accused in the Mindszenty trial of 1949. He was to be sentenced to death, but in the light of mitigating circumstances was given a 15 years prison sentence, which was reduced to 12 years. Released in February 1956, he was never rehabilitated.

Gulyás, Lajos (1918–1957) – Calvinist pastor. Pastor of the parish of Levél from 1949 until his death. After 1945 member of the Independent Smallholder Party's central committee. Resigned from his seat in 1948. On news of the Mosonmagyaróvár massacres by members of the "green ÁVO" – the border guards – during the Revolution of 1956, rushed to town, where he saved a border guard, Lajos Máté from lynching. Was indicted despite this in 1957, sentenced and executed on trumped-up charges.

Ispánki, Béla (1916–1985) – Catholic priest, college dean, later papal chamberlain. Arrested in the autumn of 1948 as one of the accused in the Mindszenty trial. Sentenced to life imprisonment in 1949, which was later commuted to 15 years. Freed in 1956. Went to Austria to organize food supply for the revolutionaries. Was unable to return. Died as Hungarian chaplain in London.

Kálló, Ferenc (1894–1944) – Catholic priest, army chaplain. Founding member in 1933 of the Ottokár Prohászka Society. Openly avowed anti-war and anti-Nazi views. In 1942 took part in organizing the Hungarian Historical Commemorative Committee. After the country's Nazi occupation, became an active member of the resistance movement's Buda group. Hid and supplied with false papers prisoners-of-war, deserters and Jews in the Eleventh Garrison Hospital. On October 28, 1944 abducted, tortured and shot to death by Arrow Cross henchmen.

P. Kiss, László Szaléz (1904–1947) – Catholic priest, Franciscan monk. In 1944 taught at the Gyöngyös Theological Academy. In 1945 founded the local Christian Democratic Youth Association, and as a Smallholder Party politician, fought against increasing communist influence. His personal tragedy began when Soviet soldiers raped a young girl in Gyöngyös. The girl's brother shot several soldiers in desperation, and organized a resistance group against the occupiers and the communist political police. He confessed this to Father Szaléz, who was arrested together with members of the group. Even though cruelly tortured, he did not break the seal of confession. Was court-martialled and executed by the Soviet authorities.

Lénárd, Ödön (1911–2003) – Member of the Piarist order, high-school teacher, secretary of the Actio Catholica. The communist dictatorship's longest-serving prisoner. First he was arrested in 1948 for protesting against the nationalization of schools. Released in 1953 by an amnesty, he was once again arrested in 1961, this time for secret clerical activities. Was sentenced to seven and a half years jail. Released once again by amnesty in 1963. Rearrested in 1966 for unlicensed clerical activities and sentenced to a total of 19 years. As the last priest in a Hungarian prison, was released in 1977 on the Pope's direct intervention.

Mindszenty, József (1892–1975) – Parish priest of Zalaegerszeg, Bishop of Veszprém, and after 1945, Archbishop of Esztergom and Primate of Hungary; made Cardinal in 1946. As Diocesan Bishop of Veszprém was arrested and taken to the notorious prison at Sopronkőhida in 1944 for openly defying the Arrow Cross regime. In 1945 spoke up against the communist dictatorship. Arrested in 1948. Sentenced to life imprisonment in 1949. Freed during the Revolution of 1956. After Soviet attack fled to the American Embassy, where he stayed in self-imposed exile until

1971. As a result of an agreement between the Vatican and the Hungarian government was allowed to leave. Died in Vienna. His mortal remains were entombed in the Basilica of Esztergom in 1991. His beatification is in progress.

Regőczi, István (1915–) – Catholic priest. In 1945-49 established an orphanage in Vác for children who had lost their parents during the war. Arrested on the charge of inculcating his pupils with anti-people's democratic sentiments. Was first taken to 60 Andrássy Road, subsequently interned at Kistarcsa. His charges were allowed to go. Released in 1953 and rearrested in 1955. Constantly harassed from 1957 until the change of regime.

Salkaházi, Sára (1899–1944) – Member of the Sisters of Social Service. In 1944 in charge of the Bokréta Street home of the Catholic Working Girls' Association. Gave asylum to, and provided the persecuted with false papers after the German occupation. Became the victim of a personal vendetta. On December 27, 1944, the Arrow Cross raided the home, took Sára Salkaházi and five others, and shot them at the Danube embankment.

Slachta, Margit (1884–1974) – Legitimist and Christian Social politician, Sister of Social Service. First female parliamentary deputy. Member of numerous Christian Socialist and Catholic female organizations. Founder of the Hungarian Sisters of Social Service. During World War II, organized international protest action against the deportation of Slovak Jewry. Harboured and saved the persecuted in the Hungarian mission's buildings. From 1945 to 1949 member of parliament. The Communist Party obstructed the functioning and activities of her party, the Christian Women's Camp; as a result she was forced to emigrate in 1949.

Soós, Géza (1912–1953) – Calvinist pastor, Foreign Ministry official, member of resistance. As leader of the Soli Deo Gloria Calvinist youth movement, aided the persecuted. He had the so-called "Auschwitz report" – a document about the systematic eradication of the Jews – translated and passed it on to the heads of the Churches in Hungary, the Zionist leadership and the Regent's daughter-in-law, Mrs. István Horthy. Member of the anti-Arrow Cross resistance. In 1946 he left the country in anticipation of a communist take-over.

Sztehló, Gábor (1909–1974) – Lutheran pastor. In 1944–1945 he sheltered several thousand persecuted children in various Protestant children's homes, saving them from deportation and the ravages of war. Founder of the first autonomous children's town. The children's homes established by him were nationalized in 1950. From 1962 until his death acted as pastor in Switzerland. A tree planted at the Jerusalem Yad Vashem honours his memory as a "Righteous Gentile".

ANTI-ARROW CROSS RESISTANCE

Bajcsy-Zsilinszky Endre (1886–1944) – Politician, publicist. As a parliamentary deputy fought relentlessly against increasing Nazi influence. On the first day of the German occupation of Hungary, drew a revolver when Gestapo thugs tried to arrest him; was dragged away wounded, and imprisoned. On October 11, 1944 was handed over to the Hungarian authorities, and released at the time of Horthy's failed attempt to disaffiliate the country from the Germans. Continued to work underground after the Arrow Cross putsch, and became President of the Hungarian National Committee for Liberation, which was in contact with all resistance groups. Arrested in November of 1944, he was sentenced to death and executed on December 23, 1944 in the prison of Sopronkőhida.

Braun, Éva (1917–1945) – Clerk, communist resistance fighter. Went underground on March 19, 1944, worked as head of the communist resistance's typographical apparatus. In the autumn of 1944 joined the armed resistance, and was a member of the Red Brigade operating independently under the aegis of the Zugló No. XIV/2 KISKA outfit (an auxiliary police unit, originally set-up by the Horthy administration for domestic law enforcement and to pre-empt a potential Arrow Cross putsch). Captured by the Arrow Cross with several of her partisan comrades on January 1, 1945, was executed at the end of the siege.

Kabók, Lajos (1884–1945) – Toolmaker, social democrat politician, trade-union leader. Parliamentary deputy between 1922 and 1935, and again from 1939 to 1944. After the Nazi occupation continued to work in the trade union movement as head of the Trades Union Council, and remained at his post even after the Arrow Cross putsch. Captured by Arrow Cross thugs on November 28, 1944. During the final days of the siege of Pest was taken from the St. István Boulevarde Arrow Cross headquarters, together with other political prisoners, in the direction of the Danube, where he was probably murdered.

Karácson, Sándor (1892–1945) – Fitter and turner, social democrat politician. Continued to work in the trade union movement even after the German occupation, to enable him to have a legal framework within which to help the persecuted. Captured by Arrow Cross thugs on November 28, 1944, together with other social democrats and union leaders. They were accused with participating in the resistance movement unfolding in the Manfred Weiss Works. Was probably murdered by Arrow Cross thugs during the final days of the siege of Pest on the Danube embankment, together with Lajos Kabók.

Kiss, János (1883–1944) – Professional soldier, lieutenant-general. Retired on May 1, 1939. After the unsuccessful attempt at secession, became military head of the Hungarian National Committee for Liberation. Arrested on November 22, 1944 by the National Retribution Organ. Taken to the notorious Margit Boulevard prison and court-martialled. Sentenced to death and executed on December 3. Posthumously promoted to colonel-general with effect from March 15, 1945.

Komoly, Ottó (1892–1945) – Zionist leader. President of the Hungarian Zionist Association from 1941. Took part from 1943 in the work of the illegal Zionist Rescue Committee, caring for the safety of several hundred, especially Polish and Slovak Jews.

After the Arrow Cross putsch continued his work at the International Red Cross. Seized and executed by an Arrow Cross detachment on January 1, 1945.

Koltói, Anna (1891–1944) – Social democrat politician. Worked at the Manfred Weiss Works at Csepel, where she became involved in the social democrat movement. 1918-1919 held trade union and civil service positions. Was interned for two years after the collapse of the Hungarian Soviet Republic. Following her release, led the women's associations of the Social Democratic Party and the Ironworkers' Union. Continued her work even after the Nazi occupation. Two days after they seized power, she was shot dead at her apartment by Arrow Cross operatives.

Kreutz, Róbert (1923–1944) – Ironworker, communist resistant fighter. As member of the Ironworkers' youth organization, carried out illegal anti-war and anti-Nazi propaganda work at the Manfred Weiss Works. In April 1944, worked as a labour serviceman at the Nagytétény aircraft factory, whence he escaped and joined the armed resistance. Member of the Görgey battalion (an anti-fascist armed resistance unit) in the autumn of 1944. Arrested by the Arrow Cross in November 1944, executed on December 24.

Kudar, Lajos (1895–1945) – Officer of the gendarmerie. Joined the military resistance during the war, took part in saving the persecuted. As head of the State Security Centre, prepared the Moscow armistice negotiations. After the Arrow Cross putsch helped to secure with his gendarmes the safety of the "protected houses" and neutral embassies. Arrested by the Gestapo at the end of 1944, executed at Buda on February 11, 1945.

Nagy, Jenő (1898–1944) – Professional soldier, colonel. Relieved of his duties in 1943, joined the resistance, where he worked under János Kiss, retired lieutenant-general. Arrested on November 22, 1944, and taken to the notorious Margit Boulevard prison. Court-martialled, sentenced to death and executed. Posthumously promoted to brigadier-general effective from March 15, 1945.

Pataky, István (1914–1944) – Fitter and turner, communist resistance fighter. Leader of the Ironworkers' youth group. Joined the resistance movement as a member of the Communist Party. In the autumn of 1944 organized an armed resistance group in the Kőbánya division of the Manfred Weiss Works, continuing his resistance activities in the Csepel factory. Arrested by the Arrow Cross in November, 1944; executed on December 24.

Pesti, Barnabás (1920–1944) – Chemical engineer, communist resistance fighter. Got involved with the anti-Nazi resistance while studying in France and joined the Communist Party in 1941. Returned to Hungary in 1943. After the Nazi occupation he first participated in manufacturing false papers and bombs, later took part in organizing armed resistance. Arrested by the Arrow Cross in November 1944, was executed at Sopronkőhida on December 24, together with Bajcsy-Zsilinszky, István Pataky and Róbert Kreutz.

Tartsay, Vilmos (1901–1944) – Professional soldier, captain. After graduating from the Military Academy, was posted to the general staff. Was pensioned off on August 1, 1941. In 1944 joined the resistance movement, working with the military wing of the Hungarian National Committee for Liberation. Arrested on November 22, 1944 by the National Retribution Organ, together with several of his associates. Taken to the Margit Boulevard prison, was sentenced to death by a military tribunal and executed on December 3, 1944. Posthumously promoted to colonel in 1945.

LABOUR-MOVEMENT VICTIMS OF THE COMMUNIST DICTATORSHIP

Demény, Pál (1901–1991) – Non-Muscovite communist politician, member of resistance. His unit hid Jews, deserters and other persecuted during World War II. Was arrested on February 13, 1945 on Rákosi's personal orders by Gábor Péter, whom Demény had previously sheltered and provided with false papers. Was first sentenced to four and a half years prison, and subsequently interned. Sentenced to ten years imprisonment in 1953 for plotting, he was released in 1956. Rehabilitated in 1989, he served from 1990 until his death as an MSZMP parliamentary deputy.

Ignotus, Pál (1901–1978) – Publicist, editor, writer. Migrated to England in 1939, where he became head of the BBC's Hungarian Department. After 1945 worked for Hungarian Embassy in London. Lured home by the communists in 1949, he was arrested by the ÁVH and accused of spying for the British Secret Service. His confession, extracted by torture, was used in the trial of the "left-wing social democrat" leaders. Ignotus was sentenced to 15 years penal servitude. Released in 1956, he returned to London after the collapse of the Revolution.

Szász, Béla (1910–1994) – Communist journalist. Joined the illegal communist movement as a university student. Migrated to France in 1937, and lived in Argentina from 1939 to 1946. Following his return to Hungary in 1946, worked as an editor, and subsequently was made head of the Foreign Ministry's (1948) and then (1949) the Ministry of Agriculture's press department. On May 24, 1949 was arrested for espionage in connection with the Rajk-case, but, despite being tortured, did not sign a confession. Sentenced to ten years imprisonment, was released on September 1, 1954 and rehabilitated. On October 5, 1956, made a speech at the reburial of László Rajk. Migrated once again in 1957, first to Vienna, finally settling in England.

Weisshaus, Aladár (1887–1963) – Clerk, non-Muscovite communist politician. Joined the social democrat movement in 1918, and from 1923 member of the Communists' Hungarian Party. Expelled from the Party in the twenties for being a so-called "factionist" and "frictionist". Arrested in 1945, was sentenced to three and a half years imprisonment on trumped-up charges in the context of one of the show trials. Despite a definitive judgment, was released only in 1956.

DEPORTED TO THE USSR

Bakay, Szilárd (1892–1947) – Professional soldier, lieutenant-general. As commander of the First Army Corps, played a significant role in preparing the attempted secession. On October 8, 1944 arrested by the Nazi Security Service. Returned from German captivity in the summer of 1945. Hauled off by the Soviet Authorities on April 11, 1946. Sentenced to death as a war criminal and executed. Rehabilitated on September 22, 1992 and posthumously promoted to colonel-general.

Bethlen, István (1874–1946) – Prime Minister of Hungary between 1921 and 1931, anti-communist, anti-Nazi politician. Opposed Hungary's excessive commitment to Germany and waging war against the USSR. Took a stand against the Jewish Laws. Supported the Kállay government's attempts at suing for a separate peace. In 1942 founded the Hungarian National Circle as a rallying centre for bourgeois forces. Had to go underground during the Nazi occupation. From the summer of 1944 pressed for establishing contact with the USSR to negotiate an armistice. Detained by the advancing Red Army, was carried off to Moscow on April 28, 1945, where he died.

Dósa, Attila (1922–1950) – Professional soldier, lieutenant in the tank corps. Wounded in World War II; worked as a driver after 1945. Established contact with the post-1945 military resistance movement. Left for Austria in 1949 and joined in the work of the Hungarian Fighters' Fraternal Society. Arrested in 1949 by the Soviets in Vienna and sentenced to 25 years in prison. Extradited to the Hungarian authorities, was sentenced to death and executed in 1950. Rehabilitated in 1990 and posthumously promoted to lieutenant-colonel.

Harangozó, Ferenc (1908–1991) – Catholic priest. After World War II helped numerous people to flee to the West. On March 11, 1948 was publicly abducted from a street in Szombathely. After months of interrogation by the KATPOL (Military-Political Department) was handed over to the Soviet authorities. His death sentence was commuted to 25 years of forced labour. Was repatriated in 1955, but released only during the 1956 Revolution. The second Soviet occupation forced him to emigrate. He became an active leader of Hungarians in Germany; for many years worked as headmaster of the Burg Kastl Hungarian high school.

Karig, Sára (1914–1999) – Author, poet, translator, social democrat politician. During World War II worked for the children's department of the Swedish Red Cross. In her capacity as a social democrat politician, protested against the so-called "blue ticket" fraud perpetrated by the communists during the parliamentary elections of August 31, 1947. Arrested by the ÁVO, was handed over to the Soviet State Security organs. Without having been sentenced, was confined to one of the most notorious forced-labour camps (Vorkuta), whence she was released in 1953.

Kovács, Béla (1908–1959) – Politician. Under Secretary for Home Affairs in the 1944 Provisional Government, 1945-46 Minister for Agriculture, 1945-47 Secretary General of the Smallholders Party. The communists launched a smear-campaign against him, accusing him of seditious acts. As the Hungarian National Assembly did not waive his parliamentary immunity, the Soviets publicly abducted him in broad daylight on February 24, 1947. He did time in a Soviet forced-labour camp, returning to Hungary in 1955. During the 1956 Revolution became one of the leaders of the newly-formed FKgP (Independent Smallholder Party), initially Minister for Agriculture and then Minister for State in the Imre Nagy government.

Lajos, Iván (1906–1953?) – Jurist, political writer. His work, Grey Book was published in 1939. In it he put forward that Hitler's Germany was not as yet fully prepared for a war. Captured by the Germans in 1944, he was carried off to Mauthausen. Returned home in June of 1945. Functioned as Counsellor in the Ministry of Education until the Soviets arrested and abducted him to the USSR in June 1946. He probably perished in 1953 in the Central-Asian gulag camp of Karaganda.

Mikó, Zoltán (1910–1945) – Professional soldier, staff captain. Joined the military resistance movement after the Arrow Cross putsch. Actively contributed to the formation of the Görgey battalion and in saving the persecuted. Furnished Gyula Illyés, Péter Veres, Imre Kovács, Lőrinc Szabó and other prominent anti-Nazis with official papers. Delivered food supplies to "protected houses". Towards the end of January 1945 was arrested by the Soviet authorities, accused of espionage, carted off to Odessa and executed. Posthumously promoted to brigadier-general in 1990.

Count Pálffy, Géza (1900–1952) – Landowner, agronomist, royalist politician, anti-Nazi resistant. Following the end of World War II initially supported the FKgP, subsequently, because of the increasingly aggressive encroachment of the communists, espoused the ideas of the Barankovics-led Democratic People's Party and Margit Slachta's Christian Women's Camp. In the summer of 1946 was arrested by the Soviet authorities, hauled off to a Siberian forced-labour camp, where he lost his life.

Ujszászy, István (1894–1948?) – Professional soldier, brigadier-general. During the 1930s served as military attaché in Warsaw and Prague. Between May 1, 1939 and August 1, 1942 head of the Second Vkf. Department (Military Intelligence Service). Appointed head of the State Security Centre on October 14, 1942 with effect from July 1. Between 1943 and 1944 sought contact with left-wing politicians and took part in "putting out feelers" towards the Western Allies. Arrested by the Germans on March 23, 1944. Demoted on charges of disloyalty by the Arrow Cross on January 18, 1945, and indicted on charges of attempting to escape. In February 1945 apprehended by the Soviet authorities. It is likely that he was returned to Budapest in 1946 or 1947, where the local Security Services imprisoned him. His subsequent fate is unknown.

Wallenberg, Raoul (1921–1947?) – Swedish diplomat in Budapest. After the autumn of 1944 saved the lives of thousands of Budapest Jews. He was mainly involved in establishing the system of protected houses, distributing protective passes and bringing back thousands from forced ditch-digging on the Austrian border. On January 16, 1945 set out from Budapest to Debrecen. Captured by the Soviets and hauled off to the USSR. His subsequent fate is uncertain; he might have died in prison or an internment camp, but it is also possible that he was murdered.

CHEKA – The Soviet political police came into being in 1917. Its first head was Dzerzhinsky. The name of the organization went through several changes (from 1922 GPU).

DISZ (Federation of Young Workers, 1950 1957) – An organization for young people between the ages of 14 and 25, under the control of the MDP. Its membership exceeded half a million.

Domokos, József (1890–1978) – Jurist. Member of the Social Democratic Party from 1912, joined the Communist Party in 1919. Lived for a while in Vienna after the collapse of the Hungarian Soviet Republic, returned home in 1925. Was carried off to the Mauthausen concentration camp after the German occupation, whence he returned in May 1945. In August of that year appointed Under-Secretary of the Ministry of Justice, and from 1949 Head of Public Prosecution. From 1954 to 1958 President of the Supreme Court. Played a significant part after 1956 in drawing up the legal parameters of retribution.

Dzerzhinsky, Felix (1877–1926) – Well-known representative of the Polish and later the Russian labour movement. Prior to 1917 spent close to a decade in jail. After the Bolshevik take-over held the offices of Commissar for Internal affairs and Commissar of Transport, and was later appointed President of the Supreme Soviet Economic Council. He earned his niche in the temple of infamy as head of the Soviet Political Police, the Cheka and later the GPU. The red terror, institutionalized by the organizations under his leadership, demanded tens of thousands of victims.

Endrédy, Vendel (1895–1981) – Cistercian monk, teacher, Abbot of Zirc. Arrested by the ÁVH in 1950. Underwent exceptionally merciless torture. Sentenced to 14 years jail as the sixth defendant in the Grősz trial. Freed on November 1, 1956 during the Revolution. Imprisoned yet again in 1957, at the end of that year was placed under police surveillance at the designated location of Pannonhalma. He lived there until his passing.

Faludy, György (1910–) – Poet, author, translator, university professor. He was arrested on trumped-up charges in 1950 and spent three years in the forced-labour camp of Recsk. His account of his camp experiences was published in his book "My Happy Days in Hell". Faludy left Hungary after the defeat of the 1956 Revolution, settling in Toronto from 1967 to 1989. He returned to Hungary after the change of regime.

JOINT, AJJDC (American Jewish Joint Distribution Committee): The aim of this overseas organization, founded in 1914, is to provide assistance to world Jewry. Its operations in Europe increased progressively from the 1930s onward, when the lives of the continent's Jews became fraught with danger. During the calamitous years of World War II it supported the persecuted and those who helped them, with significant amounts and donations.

Kádár, /Csermanek/ János (1912–1989) – Casual labourer, communist leader. Joined the Hungarian labour movement during the 1930s. Arrested twice, on the second occasion was sentenced to two years prison. From 1941, played an increasingly important role in the Hungarian labour movement. In 1943 became First Secretary of the Central Committee (KB) of the Communists' Hungarian Party (KMP). That is when he was given the nom de guerre János Kádár. Arrested once again in 1944, he soon managed to escape. From 1945 member of the Hungarian Communist Party's (MKP) Central Committee, and for a brief period Deputy-Chief Police Commissioner of Budapest. Deputy-Chief Secretary of the MKP, later MDP (1946-1950) and Interior Minister (1948-1950). In the latter capacity he played a significant role in preparing the Rajk-trial. Arrested in April 1951 by the ÁVH, Kádár was imprisoned until 1954. In 1956 was a member of Imre Nagy's government, and took part in establishing the Hungarian Socialist Workers Party (MSZMP). As part of the November 4 putsch carried out with Soviet help, he formed a puppet government. From that day on until his forced resignation in 1988, he was the number one leader of communist Hungary. Primary responsibility rests with him for the post-1956 reprisal campaign and for the execution of Imre Nagy and his associates. It was during the period bearing the stamp of his name that the country became the "jolliest barrack" in the socialist camp; this period, dubbed "goulash-communism", was characterized by a steady but slight rise in living standards, bought at the expense of the country running up considerable debts.

Kónya, Lajos (1914–1972) – Poet, writer. Became famous after 1945 as a committed poetaster of the Communist Party, who wrote his poetry according to the prevailing political "line". He wrote a poem exalting the forced resettlements; during the period of the anti-Yugoslav campaign, he composed a verse attacking the treacherous Yugoslav leaders, and at the time of the Soviet-Yugoslav reconciliation, wrote about his previous mistakes, singing the praises of the kindred Yugoslav people. Received the Kossuth prize in 1950 and 1953. Member of the writer's union, its chief secretary from 1951 to 1954 and Fellow of the Petőfi Literary Society from 1971 until his death.

Kovács, Imre (1913–1980) – Writer, politician. Member of the populist writers' movement. One of the founding members of the National Peasant Party and its First Secretary until 1946. Went underground after the Nazi occupation in 1944; his name was on the Nazi's hit list. Parliamentary deputy between 1945 and 1947. As a politician he always stood on the side of democratic understanding, and sought a rapprochement with the Smallholders Party. Resigned from the Peasant Party following the arrest of Béla Kovács. He was forced to flee the country in the autumn of 1947, and settled in the United States.

Father Kun, András (1911–1945) – Defrocked Minorite monk, Arrow Cross storm troop leader. Was expelled by his order, but did not acknowledge it. During the Arrow Cross regime, he committed a series of atrocities, murders, robberies, aggressions clad in his monk's habit. András Kun was arrested by the Arrow Cross authorities during the siege of Budapest for offences committed against soldiers and policemen. Was sentenced to death, but the punishment was not carried out. After the war the People's Court sentenced him to death by hanging; he was duly executed.

Lacisz, Martin /Sudrabs Jan/ (1888–1938) – Well-known representative of the Latvian, and later the Russian labour movement. One of the leaders of the St. Petersburg Party Committee in 1917. From December of that year Dzerzhinsky's deputy in the political police. The ideologist of bloodthirsty score-settling. As head of the Ukrainian Cheka in 1919, made extensive use of the "quota system" for executions. From the mid 1920s held minor economic posts. Executed in 1938 on Stalin's orders.

Márai, Sándor (1900–1989) – Poet, author, translator, aesthete. One of the great Hungarian thinkers of the twentieth century. His political views were always of a bourgeois-conservative nature. Spent some of his student years in Germany. Lived in Germany from 1919 to 1928, subsequently in Paris. After his return to Hungary worked as a journalist. Member of the Hungarian Academy of Sciences since 1942. After the Nazi occupation subsisted in semi-illegality because of his acknowledged anti-Nazi sentiments. Emigrated in 1948, at the time of the country's aggressive sovietization, and lived in the United States from 1952 until his passing. Was posthumously honoured with the Kossuth prize in 1990.

Népsport – Central mouthpiece of the Hungarian sports leadership from 1945 to 1990.

Peace Loan – Between 1950 and 1955 the government issued annual "Peace Loan" bonds. It was one of the state-sponsored measures used for intimidating the public. Its real aim was the deliberate depletion of purchasing power.

Péter, Gábor (1906–1993) – Journeyman tailor, all-powerful head of the communist political police. During World War II one of the leaders of the Moscow-directed Hungarian communist movement. From 1945 organizer and Chief of the Political Police Department of the

Hungarian State Police's Budapest Headquarters (PRO), later the Interior Ministry's State Security Department (ÁVO) and subsequently the State Security Authority (ÁVH). Arrested in January 1953 within the framework of the Moscow-initiated "anti-Zionist" (in fact anti-Semitic) campaign and sentenced to life imprisonment. Pardoned in 1960, he spent the rest of his years as a librarian and later in retirement in Budapest.

Pfitzner, Rudolf (1930–) – Medical student in Budapest until 1951. Took part in the work of a resistance group, distributing leaflets. Sentenced to 11 years in jail in the so-called Péterfi-Esztergár trial. Freed during the Revolution in October 1956. After the defeat of the Revolution emigrated to the German Federal Republic. Became an eminent psychologist.

Pilinszky, János (1921–1981) – One of the most significant poets of 20th-century Hungarian literature. He resisted both dictatorships. From 1949 onwards he was forced into the periphery of literary life, and was not permitted to publish anything until 1956. After 1957 he worked for the government-tolerated Catholic weekly.

Pongrátz, Gergely (1932–) – During the Revolution of 1956 he was the leader of the armed insurgent group of Corvin Lane. Following the devastating Soviet attack, he left the country in November. He relocated to Hungary in 1991.

Rákosi, Mátyás (1892–1971) – Communist Party Chief, politician. Member of the Revolutionary Governing Council during the Hungarian Soviet Republic, later Commander of the Red Guard. Fled to Vienna after the collapse of the Hungarian Soviet Republic, and having been expelled from there, left for the USSR. Worked as a member of the Comintern's Executive Committee. Was sent back to Hungary in 1924. Arrested and convicted in 1925. In 1940 was allowed to leave for the Soviet Union in exchange for the Hungarian flags seized by the Russian troops in 1849. During the war was leader of the Hungarian communist émigré group in Moscow. Was sent back to Hungary in 1945, where he became leader of the Communist Party. Apart from his brief loss of power in 1953, he was from 1947 to 1956 the number one man of the Party and the government in communist Hungary, and the principal person responsible for the rule of terror. The Rákosi era was characterized by forced resettlements, internment camps, executions, and an all- pervasive personality cult. As a consequence of Rákosi's preference for an atrocious economic policy based on exploiting agriculture in favour of speeding up the development of heavy industry, the country was on the verge of bankruptcy and the majority of the populace lived close to the subsistence level. In June 1956 he was removed from his position under Soviet pressure and recalled to the USSR. He died there in provincial exile.

Szabad Nép – Communist political daily. From 1945 to 1956 the Party's central newspaper. During the '50s, workers everywhere in Hungary had to attend the so-called "Szabad Nép-half hours", when the more important articles were communally discussed for propaganda purposes.

Szálasi, Ferenc (1897–1946) – Professional army officer, Arrow Cross "Leader of the Nation". Expelled from the Army in 1933 for subversive activities. After several prison sentences and attempts at forming a party, became the acknowledged leader of the Arrow Cross mass movement by 1939. His movement lost significance during the war years. Came to power with Nazi help on October 15, 1944. Introduced total dictatorship, supported by Arrow Cross terrorism. The terror caught up with those Jews, who had escaped the earlier deportations. As a result of the Arrow Cross dictatorship the entire country was turned into a theatre of war. As the end approached, Szálasi fled to Austria, where he was captured by the Americans. Extradited to Hungary, the People's Court sentenced him to death by hanging in 1946.

Upper Hungary – Following the First World War, the Northern part of historic Hungary was appropriated by Czechoslovakia under the terms of the 1920 Treaty of Trianon. In 1938, as a result of the First Vienna Award, the Hungarian-inhabited Southern areas were re-annexed to Hungary, but the post-World War Two Paris Treaty once again handed it back to Czechoslovakia.

The House of Terror Museum has been commissioned in 2002 by Director-General MÁRIA SCHMIDT with the support of Prime Minister VIKTOR ORBÁN, according to the plans of JÓZSEF SZÁJER and ATTILA VÁRHEGYI. Historical concept: MÁRIA SCHMIDT. Visual concept: ATTILA F. KOVÁCS. Music: ÁKOS KOVÁCS. Building reconstruction: JÁNOS SÁNDOR, KÁLMÁN ÚJSZÁSZY. Implementation: Architekton Rt. Associates: Zoltán Csáki, Tibor Fabiny, Sándor Fábry, István Fehérváry, Jenő Fónay, György Haraszti, Miklós Horváth, István Ihász, Pál Illés, Attila Janovitz, Frigyes Kahler, Csaba Kardos, Gábor Kiszely, Miklós Kun, Katalin Kutrucz, Sándor Ladányi, László Makai, György Markó, Gusztáv Menczer, Gyula Mészáros, István Őri Kiss, Sándor Szakács, András Szalai, Károly Szerencsés, István Vonnák.

The catalogue was prepared in 2003 with the support of the Ministry of National Cultural Heritage and the National Cultural Endowment Program. Published by the Public Endowment for Research in Central and East-European History and Society. Edited by Mária Schmidt. English translation by Ann Major. Designed by Kissík Grafikai Stúdió. Photographs by János Szentiváni, Gyula Zácsfalvi (p. 23). Photograph processing by Timp Stúdió. Separation by Reaktor Kft. Printing by JAVIPA Nyomda, Békéscsaba. Binding by Dürer Nyomda, Gyula. Person in charge: Pál Such.